The 4.15 To Cartsdyke!

'The 4.15 to Cartsdyke!' Locomotive 'Cartsburn No. 2' at the head of the fitting-out Basin, Scotts' shipyard, beside the foremen shipwrights' shed, 1948.

The 4.15 To Cartsdyke!

A Tale of Two Shipyards:–
Scotts' and the Greenock Dockyard

by

Michael Dick

The Pentland Press Limited
Edinburgh · Cambridge · Durham

© M. Dick 1993

First published in 1993 by
The Pentland Press Ltd.
1 Hutton Close
South Church
Bishop Auckland
Durham

ISBN 1 85821 053 4

Typeset by Elite Typesetting Techniques, Southampton.
Printed and bound by Antony Rowe Ltd., Chippenham.

To the men of Scotts' and the Greenock Dockyard

Acknowledgements

Thanks are due to *The Herald* for consent to reproduce the series of short articles from the 1960s.

The *Greenock Telegraph* was essential for background information and for providing two illustrations from their collection.

Thanks to Mrs Lesley Couperwhite, Librarian, Inverclyde District Libraries, for permitting ready access to past volumes of the *Greenock Telegraph*.

My appreciation to Scott Lithgow Ltd. for permission to use so many of their photographs.

The *Appendix of Ships* would have been impossible to collate without the use of *Marine News*, the journal of the World Ship Society. The Central Record of the Society has been invaluable in providing details and fate of several vessels.

The book could not have been written without the contribution of former workers and management of Scotts' and The Greenock Dockyard.

Michael Dick.
January 1993.

Contents

Sources

Periodicals/Newspapers

Marine News
Sea Breezes
Ships Monthly
Glasgow Herald
Greenock Telegraph

Texts

Better by Yards, Colin Castle, Murdoch Carberry, 1988.
The Clyde Puffer, Dan McDonald, David & Charles, 1977.
Clyde Shipbuilding from old photographs, Moss & Hume, Batsford, 1975.
Clyde Shipwrecks, Moir & Crawford, 1988.
Gathering of the Clans, Middlemiss, Shield Publications, 1988.
Growth and Decline of Clyde Shipbuilding, Moss (pamphlet), 1986.
Half of Glasgow's Gone, Michael Dick, Brown Son & Ferguson, 1986.
Ships of the Clyde, H. M. Le Fleming, Ian Allan, 1960.
Song of the Clyde, Walker, Patrick Stephens, 1984.
Steel Shipbuilding, Walker, Shire Publications, 1981.
Two Hundred and Fifty Years of Shipbuilding, James Jack Advertising, 1961.
The Shipbuilders, George Blake, Faber & Faber, 1935.
Willie Rough (drama), Bill Bryden, Southside Publishers Ltd., 1972.

Individuals

Clyde pilots
Clyde tugmen
Greenock Dockyard, former managers and employees
Scotts' S. B. & E. Co., Ltd., former managers and employees
Scott Lithgow, former managers and employees

Photographs

Author
Bob Pollok
Cory Towage
Crusader Insurance
Jim Prentice
Scottish Development Agency
Scott Lithgow
The Scottish Records Office
Sunday Mail

List of Illustrations

Foreword

Scotts' and The Greenock Dockyard were the most recent Greenock shipyards still in existence, albeit operating latterly as the Cartsburn and
Cartsdyke segments of the Scott Lithgow consortium which extended to
Port Glasgow. By the mid 1980s both yards lay derelict and the demolition stage was completed by 1988.

There are few people in the Inverclyde District without memories of
these yards, either through a direct or indirect connection. If they did not
work there, they knew someone who did.

For much of the twentieth century these yards operated alongside each
other. (Scotts' of course was much larger and had the reputation as possibly the oldest shipyard in the world; the Dockyard built most of the Clan
Line fleet.) Both were an integral part of the local community, being
referred to as 'The Yards'.

Clyde shipbuilding has been the subject of many books and there was
even one commemorating the 250th anniversary of Scotts' published in
1961. But this is not a definitive history and I have attempted to go beyond
the mere recording of facts, to search for the innermost being. 'The Yards'
meant a great deal to people and I have tried to record something of this
rich heritage before it becomes forgotten.

My sources have been many and varied, illustrative and written, but
where possible I have tried to get the accounts of the people who worked
there.

The content is centred mainly on the postwar period.

An aerial view of Scotts' shipyard with Greenock Dockyard and the James Watt Dock to the right, 1964. The Victoria Harbour is to the extreme left.

Chapter 1

Reflections

I last sailed down the Clyde in 1987 on board the *Waverley*. She did not leave from Bridge Wharf, South Side, the traditional departure point for down-river cruises; instead the paddler left from Anderston Quay on the north bank of the River, much further down from the dilapidated Bridge Wharf.

The sheds, cranes, docks and varied shipping, which had been such an established feature of Glasgow Harbour in its heyday, simply did not exist anymore. A mile or so down from Anderston Quay, on the opposite bank, was the vast, infilled Prince's Dock site being prepared for the 1988 Glasgow Garden Festival. The Scottish Exhibition and Conference Centre dominated the former Queen's Dock site and lay behind the massive Stobcross or Finnieston crane which still provided a legacy of Glasgow's maritime past.

In the midst of Govan, Harland & Wolff's old shipyard had long since been transformed into a housing development and shipbuilding had ended there in 1963. However, despite the extensive landscaping, I could still make out where the crane ramps and building berths used to be. Further downriver there was still considerable industry on the old Fairfield site, although Fairfield as such had gone into liquidation in 1965 and there were further traumas under U.C.S. before a rescue giving long-term security was established under Govan Shipbuilders.[1]

In 1987 there was little sign of Alexander Stephen's Linthouse yard which lay adjacent to Fairfield. Such had been the activity on this stretch that it used to be known as 'The Golden Mile'. Nothing remained of the formerly congested industry on the North bank. This had been the

---

[1] Since 1988 Kvaerner (Govan).

Development of Laing Homes housing estate on the infilled Kingston Dock site, 1987.

Development in former dockland with particular emphasis on the site of Glasgow Garden Festival, 1988.

Govan Shipbuilders yard, 1983; now Kvaerner (Govan), the last merchant ship-builders on the Upper Reaches.

epicentre at one time of Clyde shipbuilding and spanned a one-and-a-half mile beat of river bank. I remembered the way it was in 1960, on a previous sail, when the narrowness of the murky river was emphasised by the Linthouse yard, on the south side, almost directly opposite Barclay Curle's Whiteinch yard; the lofty tower cranes poised over the occupied berths; the scaffolding which webbed the numerous hulls on the stocks; the sparks which rained down from the welders' torches; the cheery waves from the workers who acknowledged our greetings; it had all been so noisy and exciting with an air of apparent permanence. And then the signs with the words DEAD SLOW painted in large lettering and stuck on to supports by the shore in front of the yards. Again from 1960, I recalled the thump of the *Caledonia's* paddles reducing in frequency and the steamer almost drifted past the yard in question as she complied with the sign's request.

The memories came flooding back to me as I observed this stretch from the deck of the *Waverley* in 1987. The contrast was quite dramatic – the waterfront had been cleared substantially of all shipbuilding plant; only the odd crane stood in isolation; in places only the end of a slipway at the water's edge gave a hint of the heavy industry which had featured here for so long. However, there was a whiff of shipbuilding on the north bank in

A heyday scene from John Brown's, 1966. The cargo liner Glenfinlas *and Cunarder* Queen Elizabeth 2 *under construction.*

H.M.S. Norfolk *fitting-out at Yarrow's in 1987, shortly after her launch. Yarrow is one of only two yards building ships on the Upper Reaches.*

the form of Yarrow of Scotstoun where warship production continued and the frigate *Norfolk* was fitting out, not long after her launch.

I reflected on the sudden demise of that cluster of shipyards – Stephen's had completed their last ship in 1967; Barclay Curle had launched their last ship in 1967; Charles Connell, latterly as the Scotstoun Division of U.C.S., built their last ship in 1975; Blythswood stopped construction in 1964. It was so quiet in 1987, both on shore and in the water where the only sound was the rhythmic beat of paddles.

A forest of cranes with jibs jutting in various directions indicated the site that had been John Brown's yard at Clydebank. As we passed the slipway where the famous 'Queens' were built, I noticed that much of the original equipment was still *in situ.* Shipbuilding had ended here in 1972 when Brown's went down with U.C.S., with the maritime connection since restricted to the building of oil-related platforms.

As we sailed past Erskine my mind went back again to trips I had made in the 1960s. It had been so annoying then not to get a clear view of Denny's yard, obstructed by Dumbarton Rock. But it did not matter in 1987 as Denny's had gone into liquidation as long ago as 1962. There had always been a hiatus of sorts after Clydebank, with no more concentrated shipbuilding until the Lower Reaches at Port Glasgow. But in 1987 Lower Clyde activity was negligible and there was no resurgence of adrenalin or anticipation as we swung towards the southern bank at Cardross Bend.

Ferguson's small yard at Port Glasgow, adjacent to the medieval Newark Castle, operated as the Appledore-Ferguson combine and had a ferry order in hand. The Port Glasgow branch of Scott Lithgow, itself spawned from a merger of the successful Lithgow's and Scotts' yards in 1968, was inactive. Under the ownership since 1984 of Trafalgar House Offshore the last rig had been launched and the mammoth, green-painted gantry crane straddled the empty berth which had seen the launch of several supertankers in the 1970s. I contemplated the site of Hamilton's old yard which until the early 1960s had launched some fine cargo liners.

Scott Lithgow's former Cartsdyke yard went by. As The Greenock Dockyard this yard had churned out quality vessels for the Clan Line, production being almost conveyor-belt-like. The berths, heavily concreted, could be easily made out and were dominated on either side by ramps with two pairs of cranes servicing each berth. The cranes seemed relatively small, and showed some signs of rust with bushes and small trees between the berths adding to the air of neglect. With other local yards the Cartsdyke concern had used the adjacent James Watt Dock for

Launch day for Brocklebank's Makrana *at Hamilton's yard, Port Glasgow, 1957. Many of the Brocklebank Line's ships were launched without ceremony and were officially named on delivery at the home port of Liverpool.*

fitting out their ships and had leased the Garvel Dry Dock from the end of the nineteenth century.

We steamed on past Scotts' former Cartsburn complex. There was not much time to take it all in but to the east was a series of sheds built at right angles to the water and which actually encroached the water's edge. The sheds were black-painted and emblazoned across two of them was the faded white lettering forming the words SCOTTS' CARTSBURN DOCKYARD. There were two obviously large berths towards the centre of the yard and one, not so clear, to the east end but much smaller. There was extensive concrete covering almost the entire site. Cranes varied in age and size but generally were much larger-looking then their less solid Cartsdyke counterparts and included some superb examples of the tower crane which had been such an important feature of the British shipyard in its heyday. The jibs of all but one of the light-blue painted cranes pointed east; again there were signs of dilapidation but this site was not so overgrown as neighbouring Cartsdyke; an uneven but unbroken line of shedding lay towards the rear of the bare berths.

Cartsdyke and Cartsburn had the appearance of an industrial museum in 1987, preserved in a time warp. Here was an acknowledgement to an era

Scott Lithgow's abandoned Cartsdyke yard, 1987.

Scott Lithgow's derelict Cartsburn yard, 1987. This was best known as Scotts'.

now past, although they could have been yards lying dormant in the Depression of the early 1930s waiting to be reactivated when the trade cycle improved. But the SLOW signpost at the end of the Cartsburn fitting-out basin could be ignored. No more ships would be built at Greenock and, while musing, it came to me that Scotts' was reputed to be the oldest shipyard in the world. The *Waverley* soon pulled into Customhouse Quay, Greenock, and my cruise ended.

In his book *The Shipbuilders*, depicting the Depression on Clydeside, George Blake described the same downriver stretch. In the Upper Reaches he wrote about the 'deserted ways and static gantries.' As the yards went by, 'the berths empty, the grass growing about the sinking keel blocks.' He went on to describe Govan as 'looking like a bloody cemetery.' John Brown, who from December 1931 had 3,000 men laid off, 'with the monstrous red hull of No. 534[2] looming in its abandonment like a monument to the glory departed.' He referred to 'the vast desolation of Beardmore's at Dalmuir closed for good.' On the Lower Reaches, 'two tramp steamers building at Port Glasgow stood out like monuments in the long range of silent yards. Greenock's heart lay bare and bleeding.

---

[2] *Queen Mary.*

Caird's was closed for good.' And he wrote about the 'disappearing traditions, glory and passion which were visible in decay.'

Yet the Clyde bounced back from this nadir and in 1934 over 237,000 tons were launched.

In fact, the industry had never been a very secure one. Although output in 1913 reached almost 777,000 tons, booms and slumps had figured prominently from 1870. Shipbuilding demand was subjected to world trade cycles. In November 1874 the Clyde Shipbuilding Association intimated that 'the present position of trade justified the reduction of the rate of wages by fifteen per cent'.[3] A major strike in 1877 resulted in a lockout lasting for eight months, involving 10,000 men. In September 1878 during a world depression J. E. Scott, owner of the Cartsdyke shipyard in Greenock, went bankrupt.

In 1925 launches were as low as 78,441 tons and by 1928 Clyde yards and other U.K. yards were in dire straits. At the height of the Depression 1929-1933 work on '534' was halted after Cunard could not agree terms with the government for more subsidy. Rescue operations included from 1929 capacity cuts of nineteen per cent with seven yards closed and two mothballed.

The list of yards in operation on the River in 1960 was extensive:– Harland & Wolff, D. & W. Henderson, A. & J. Inglis, Fairfield, Alexander Stephen, Barclay Curle, Charles Connell, Blythswood, Yarrow, Simons, Lobnitz, Fleming & Ferguson (Paisley), John Brown, Scott (Bowling), William Denny – all on the Upper Reaches. And on the Lower Reaches:– James Lamont, Ferguson, Lithgow's East Yard, William Hamilton, Lithgow's Kingston Yard, George Brown, Greenock Dockyard, Scotts'. In all twenty-three yards and some of these also had extensive repair facilities.

However, by 1962 most Upper Clyde yards were experiencing great losses – on fixed-price contracts; productivity was poor and material costs were rising. This crisis, which heightened in the mid-1960s, caught the yards unprepared and there was to be no recovery this time. Tortuous consortium arrangements, mergers, nationalisation and finally privatisation in the 1980s only postponed the inevitable demise of shipbuilding on the Clyde as a whole.

But Scotts' and The Greenock Dockyard, under Scott Lithgow survived longer than most and into the 1980s. Blake had referred to the town of Greenock having its 'heart torn out to make room for ships'. His descrip-

---

[3] Growth and decline of Clyde shipbuilding.

tion of Greenock during the Depression, 'its heart lay bare and bleeding', was even more appropriate at the end of the last decade.

I went back to newspaper reports from the 1960s. These extracts from the *Glasgow Herald* included the following details of Orders, Launches and Trials for products of The Greenock Dockyard and Scotts'.

From 1963:

CLYDE TO BUILD THREE CARGO SHIPS

The order is for three[4] refrigerated cargo motorships to be built by the Greenock Dockyard Company Ltd., Greenock, for the British & Commonwealth Shipping Co., London. Each of the 10,000-ton ships is worth around £1.75 m. This is the third three-ship contract which has been won by the highly modernised Greenock yard over the last two years.

They are working on three ships[5] which were ordered by British & Commonwealth a little over a year ago for chartering to the South African Marine Corporation. This work is so well advanced that the preparation of the steel plate for the first of the new ships can begin by the middle of next month. Construction of the first ship can start in January. The labour force of about 800 men are now assured of full employment for nearly two years.

From December 1962:

GREENOCK DOCKYARD LAUNCH

The Clyde will have a visit this week from Mrs. Marples, wife of the Minister of Transport, who is to launch the cargo motorship *Clan Macgowan* on Friday at Greenock. The ship will complete a trio[6] of fast 9,000-ton ships built for the British & Commonwealth group which includes the Clan Line.

---

[4] *Clan Ramsay; Clan Ranald; Clan Robertson.*

[5] *Letaba; Drakenstein* (nicknamed *Frankenstein*); *Tzaneen.*

[6] *Clan Macgillivray; Clan Macgregor.*

From July 1966:

SCOTTS' FIRST LAUNCH AT CARTSDYKE YARD

The first launch at the Cartsdyke yard, Greenock, since it was taken over in April from the Greenock Dockyard Company Ltd., by Scotts' Shipbuilding & Engineering Co. Ltd., took place yesterday – the 8,100-ton refrigerated banana carrier, *Geesthaven*, built for the Geest Industries Ltd., of Spalding, Lincolnshire.

Named by Mrs. Maarten Van Geest, the new ship is a sister to the *Geestcape*, launched from the same yard in March and due for trials in about six weeks.

The ships, which will have a service speed of twenty-one knots, are part of an expansion to Geest Industries to keep pace with the increasing production of bananas in the Windward Islands, currently supplying one half of Britain's banana imports.

The last ship to be launched by Greenock Dockyard Co. – the banana carrier Geestcape *on her launch day in 1966. The ship under construction in the adjacent berth is the* Geesthaven. *From 1/4/66 the Dockyard became the Cartsdyke Shipyard of the Scotts' group.*

From April 1967:

CLYDE-BUILT SHIP FOR GERMAN FIRM

The first ship to be built on the Clyde for German owners since the war, the fast banana carrier *Parma*, is the first of two sisterships ordered by F. Laeisz of Hamburg and the ship was named by Mrs. Eike Reemtsma, wife of a Director of the owning company.

The *Parma* has a length of 501 feet and deadweight of 6,000 tons. The owners now operate only fruit carriers but were famous around the turn of the century for their fast sailing ships known as the 'Flying P' Line. Most of their sailing ships were built in German yards, but among those bought from other owners and renamed was the first *Parma*, formerly the *Arrow* built at Port Glasgow.

From 1967:

SHIP ON TRIALS

On the Lower Reaches of the River, Scotts' of Greenock have handed over the cargo liner *Clan Alpine*[7] to her owners Clan Line Steamers. Although this is the first ship to be built under the title of Scotts' for these owners it is the 67th vessel to be built either for the Clan Line or the British & Commonwealth Company at Greenock.

The previous ships were built by the Greenock Dockyard Co., now merged with the Scotts' group and known as Scotts' Cartsdyke Shipyard.

From 1963:

SUBMARINE ORDER FOR THE CLYDE

An order for two 'Oberon'[8] class submarines, worth about £6.5 m, has been placed with Scotts' Shipbuilding & Engineering Company Ltd., Greenock, by the Royal Australian Navy.

---

[7] The *Clan Alpine* was the first *Clan* liner and also the name of the last.

---

[8] Otway, Oxley.

The order adds to a run of successes by the Greenock firm in the past three months, during which they have already obtained orders worth nearly £7 m. They have now sufficient work to ensure employment for their shipyard and engine works for two years. It was stated that delivery of the first submarine would be in 1966 with the second following a year later.

Mr. John Lee, Director and Secretary of the Greenock firm, calculated the order on top of those for a bulk carrier[9] of 28,000 tons obtained in July and a £5.5 m fleet replenishment ship[10] in August, would provide continuity of employment for the bulk of the labour force for the next two years and considerably longer for the submarine squads.

A total of about 2,500 men are employed in the shipyard and engine works.

From October 1962:

LAUNCH AT SCOTTS'

Scotts' Shipbuilding & Engineering Company, Greenock, are to launch the submarine *Otus* tomorrow and the naming ceremony will be performed by Lady Carroll, wife of Sir John Carroll, Deputy Controller (Research & Development) at the Admiralty. The *Otus* is one of the 'Oberon' class of attack submarines with superstructure built mainly of glass fibre laminate. Diesel driven and capable of high underwater speeds, she is equipped for continuous submerged operations and will have homing torpedoes.

Scotts' also built the sister submarine *Otter* and two of the earlier 'Porpoise' class, *Cachalot* and *Walrus*, of which the 'Oberon' class is a development.

From 1963:

BULK CARRIER FOR PANAMA

A bulk carrier of 28,000 tons deadweight for a Greek-controlled

---

[9] *Graigwerrd.*

---

[10] *Resource.*

shipping company is on trials this week.

The bulk carrier *Kapetan Georgis*, was built by Scotts' Ship-building & Engineering Company, Greenock, for the Virgo Steamship Company of Panama, controlled by the Greek ship-owner Mr. Stratus G Andreadis. This is the £1.4 m order which Scotts' announced at their 250th anniversary celebrations in October 1961.

It is the largest merchant ship built at the Cartsburn yard, being 570 feet long and 82.5 feet broad. The *Kapetan Georgis* will have a speed of 15 knots.

From 1962:

GUINEA TO ORDER MORE SHIPS

The Government of Guinea, who took delivery of their first

Scotts' modernised Cartsburn complex in 1964, showing a bulk carrier and submarine under construction and a bulk carrier and submarine fitting-out.

ocean-going merchant ship, the 15,000-ton bulk carrier, *Simandou*, after successful trials in the Clyde yesterday, intend to order other ships to handle their developing exports.

Mr. D. B. Couyate, Director of Guinea Transport, said after the trials that he was more than satisfied with the ship's performance and the excellent workmanship of Scotts' of Greenock.

More than 60 of Scotts' workmen gave up the first half-day of their annual holidays to complete the trials of the *Simandou* which were delayed for two days at the request of the Guinea representatives.

Chapter 2

Evolution

Greenock Dockyard had its origins in 1900 when the Grangemouth Dockyard became established in mid-Cartsdyke. For eight years this establishment was known as the Grangemouth & Greenock Dockyard Co., and the nickname 'Klondyke' was applied to this yard. In 1894 the Klondike discovery in Canada brought the first of 100,000 gold-seeking fortune hunters to Alaska. Most of the early miners struck it rich.

In the early twentieth century the owners of the Dockyard soon established what was to be a long-lasting reputation for frugality and economy with a 'waste not, want not' philosophy. On one occasion when inspecting the yard, the owner was appalled at the quantity of discarded nuts, bolts and other material strewn carelessly about. He was attributed to exclaim to the offending labour force, 'Do you think this is Klondike?' The name stuck with the minor adaptation to 'Klondyke'.

In 1908, as the Greenock side of the operation was the bigger, the name was changed to the Greenock & Grangemouth Dockyard Co. In 1924 Cazyer Irvine & Co. acquired a majority shareholding and by the 1940s one of their subsidiaries owned the yard.

The yard's reputation for economy developed apace from the early 1920s but, to be fair, from the point of view of cargo ship construction, in those days competition between shipyards was intense and survival was only ensured by operating on a shoe-string budget. The adjacent Scotts' yard was in a more fortunate position, with their 'bread and butter' merchant work being supplemented by a large naval order book, and thus could function on a more leisurely basis.

Continuity of work was absolutely essential as there could be a three-month period between winning an order and laying the keel, after drawings and ordering of equipment had been done. Single orders were of no real benefit and even a two-ship order involved an element of stress for the yard's administration.

Apparently in the early 1920s the order situation was really poor as the Dockyard launched no ships in 1923 and only two sailing barges in 1924. In the period of the Depression a cargo ship lay on the stocks from 1930 until 1934. The Dockyard in common with other yards at the time was reluctant to install new machinery and much was obtained secondhand from yards which had closed. Indeed, much material was had from Beardmore's in 1930 at a great bargain price. Plant was taken away piecemeal and re-erected.

Dockyard production for the Clan Line was prolific and, of twenty-three ships ordered by the Line between 1924 and 1945, that shipyard built all twenty-three. The *Greenock Telegraph* reported in 1938 that:

'Greenock Dockyard Company have the busiest establishment in cargo ship construction on the Clyde, six vessels of 10,000 tons deadweight being on order from the Clan Line.'

The launch of the Clan Campbell *from Greenock Dockyard on 14/1/37. The buoy tender* Torch *is in the right background.*

The Clan Campbell *leaving for trials in 1937, in tow of the* Wrestler.

And then there was the tremendous volume of repair work done by the Dockyard in the course of World War II. Much of this was concerned with minor damage caused by convoy collision. However, the *Blairspey*, which had been torpedoed in the North Atlantic in 1940, required a completely new forepeak. It was also noted that during wartime over 1,200 men were employed in the Dockyard.

In the years immediately after World War II there were continued food shortages and widespread rationing still applied. However, the sugar shortage did not concern the Dockyard plumbers who were engaged on routine repair work in the James Watt Dock. When working on the sugar boats these tradesmen barrowed pipes between the yard and the dock, packed brown sugar into the pipes and then made the return trip to the yard where the sugar was distributed into eager hands.

The yard went on to construct twenty-nine out of the thirty-eight ships ordered for the Clan Line between 1946 and 1967. The remainder were ordered elsewhere only because the Dockyard was too heavily committed and did not have the available building capacity.

One former yard manager described the Dockyard in the 1950s as approaching a shipbuilding museum of the prewar period. The facilities were still for wholly-riveted construction and the existing lifting equipment and other machines had been strained by the building of some very heavy-scantlinged Heavy Lift ships during the war. Some welded units were put on post-war tankers but with great difficulty. Apart from a ten-ton hammer-head crane and three five-tonners, the berths were served by 'jiggers' or 'sheer legs' which looked and were operated like a ship's derrick. Even at that time there were reports of equipment being borrowed from other yards. It was common practice for head foremen to borrow from other head foremen at local shipyards due to late delivery of certain items. The borrowed items were replaced when they became available again.

However, modernisation plans were soon underway. Initially it was decided to have three crane tracks serving the two new berths but the later rejection of this plan proved to be a blessing in disguise. The Chairman of the owning company, whose shipping interests also included the Union Castle Line, wished the yard to be capable of building that Line's intermediate passenger liners at Cartsdyke and a central craneway would have limited the width of berth required for these ships. It was also considered that two tracks were more economical and so the full plans did not materialise. But after amalgamation with Scotts' in 1966 and later Lithgow in 1970, Cartsdyke was able to construct bulk carriers and tankers with a breadth of over eighty feet.

The new berths were serviced by 4×25-ton travelling cranes manufactured by Butters Brothers and were of similar design to cranes already in operation at Denny's Dumbarton yard. Similar cranes of this and higher capacity were used by three or four yards on the Clyde and in England. It had been originally proposed to have 4×15-tonners but this would have entailed a new design and the cost would have been prohibitive. The cranes were very manoeuvrable but the aluminium jib had to be inspected annually and cleaned to prevent corrosion and sometimes the jib had to be lowered for treatment. The adjacent crane would assist with the jib lowering.

The modernisation began in 1958 and was completed in 1964 when it was announced in this *Glasgow Herald* report:

'Since the completion of their modernisation programme, the Greenock Dockyard Co., Ltd. has been a "two-berth" yard (previously there had been three berths) with ability to build ships of up to 600 feet in length and 24,000 tons deadweight.'

Modernisation, completed in the early 1960s, enabled much larger vessels to be constructed at Cartsdyke. Launch day for the bulk carrier World President *at Scotts' Cartsdyke yard, 1969.*

John Scott set up a shipyard in the Westburn area of Greenock in 1711 and, in common with most other Lower Clyde yards which developed at that time, Scott concentrated on the building of small craft which would ply mainly on the Firth of Clyde and west coast of Scotland – smacks, fishing skiffs, herring busses, lighters and gabberts. The latter were the fore runners of the Clyde 'puffer'.

Many of these yards were of a very temporary basis, in fact being 'one-ship' yards with only a few employees. They certainly mushroomed but over the long-term the ninety or so recorded firms could be reduced to some ten which operated on a more permanent basis. Throughout the eighteenth century few of the Clyde yards built a sailing vessel of any significance.

Scotts' built their first drydock in 1767 and another major step was the acquisition of an iron and brass foundry in 1825, thus initiating the marine engineering connection. In 1904 this entity was totally integrated into the shipbuilding side as 'Scotts' Shipbuilding & Engineering Co., Ltd.'

Naval construction developed in the second half of the nineteenth century and strong links with Alfred Holt and John Swire resulted in considerable merchant ship orders over the next century. A major 'first' was the building of the *Ajax, Achilles* and *Agamemnon* for Holt's and their Dutch associates' Far Eastern trade. Their efficient steam engine, reducing fuel-consumption, enabled them to compete with sailing ships over long voyages.

Other significant construction was the four-masted barque *Archibald Russell* in 1905, the first submarine depot ship *Maidstone* in 1910 and, although submarine production on the Clyde has always been fairly limited, Scotts' established a sound reputation from 1912 when the first submarine to be ordered in Scotland, S1, was laid down. They even built a tanker in 1928 with superstructure all-aft which, of course, was quite unusual in those days.

At the beginning of the twentieth century the yard was firmly based at Cartsburn; the Carts burn actually flowed into the Clyde at Scotts' Cartsburn yard. Scotts' also had a foothold in Cartsdyke which was a Burgh annexed by Greenock in 1840. In 1934 further expansion took place. Scotts' yard at Cartsdyke East was separated from the main Cartburn establishment by the Greenock Dockyard Co. Ltd. and a deal was negotiated with the Dockyard, which moved east, and Scotts' took over Cartsdyke Mid-Yard. There are those even now who maintain that the Dockyard lost out on the deal, relinquishing an excellent location for the launching of ships. Nevertheless, this move gave Scotts', after 200 years, an unbroken water-frontage.

During World War II Scotts' built solely for the Royal Navy, to the exclusion of merchant shipping, and warship construction reached almost fifty vessels. The yard suffered considerable damage during the Greenock Blitz in May 1941 and the effect was recorded in *250 Years of Shipbuilding*:

> 'Scotts' head office was burned to the ground, all records were lost, together with a great number of old pictures, ship models and documents of great historical interest. The engine works, too, were affected but in the space of six months the work was again in full swing.
>
> 'A destroyer, the hull of which was plated and approaching the launching stage, was blown off the keel blocks and had to be taken apart and rebuilt. A submarine on the next berth was moved bodily some inches on the blocks but by means of jacks and willing workers was replaced without damage. Another bomb came through the West boundary wall, just missing a destroyer in drydock. Yet another bomb burst under the stern of a cruiser on the building berth but, though it blew some cast-iron keel blocks through the roof of the platers' shed thirty yards away, did no damage to the ship.
>
> 'All electric power was cut off for several days and power had to be supplied to the yard by one of H.M. submarines, assisted by portable, petrol-driven generators.'

There were major postwar developments in the yard and again taken from the same source:

> 'By 1948 the shipyard administration office was converted into Head Office building, embracing Directors' Rooms, Board Room, Secretary's Department, Costing and Accounting Department, Estimating and Buying Offices and a Directors' and Officials' Lunch Room.
>
> 'New welding bays and toilets were constructed in 1954 and the old toilets were dismantled.
>
> 'The office restoration was completed in 1957 with the erection of the Engine Works administration and design and drawing office buildings. An Apprentice Training Centre was established in 1948.
>
> 'In 1960 in response to a Factory Act which demanded adequate washing facilities, a Welfare Building was constructed at

the head of the Fitting-Out Basin with washing facilities and clothes-hanging arrangements for one-third of the workforce. In addition showers and changing facilities were also provided.'

The berth situation was also reappraised and considerable expansion and modernisation took place. The centre-piece of this development, announced in 1958, was to be the instalment of two giant travelling cranes capable of lifting forty-ton loads within a radius of 150 feet and sixty tons at a smaller radius. The cranes were to operate on a large ramp extending approximately the full length of the berths which were to be extended to provide for the construction of a ship of 24,000 dwt. tons and two of 19,000 dwt. tons or alternatively one of 24,000 tons and one of 40,000 dwt. tons. Two of the existing six twelve-ton cranes were to be dismantled leaving four twelve-ton, two twenty-ton and the two new forty-ton cranes to provide the lifting facilities on the berths. The existing Admiralty

Two giant travelling cranes – the centre-piece of the major development on Scotts', 1961; a line of keel blocks can be seen clearly on the right berth.

berths were to remain, in addition to the reorganised berths. The rebuilding was to be completed in 1961.

The two small gardens in the centre of the yard were built to commemorate the visit of Prince Philip for the 250th anniversary celebrations on 16th October 1961. A plaque recorded the visit.

There was further expansion on 1966. On 21st December 1965 it was announced[1] in the national press that:

> 'The Cartsdyke Shipyard of the Greenock Dockyard Co. Ltd. is to be merged with the adjoining yard of Scotts' Shipbuilding & Engineering Co. Ltd.'

The new enlarged yard was now under control of Scotts' and the British & Commonwealth holding was now sold to them. While the changeover from the Greenock Dockyard to Scotts' was taking place, the two ships completing for the Geest Line were handed over by the Cartsdyke Dock-

The Geestcape *on trials in 1966. While the changeover from Greenock Dockyard to Scotts' was taking place, the* Geestcape *and her sister ship* Geesthaven *were handed over by the Cartsdyke Dockyard Co., Ltd.*

[1] *Glasgow Herald.*

yard Co., Ltd. The ships were the *Geestcape* and *Geesthaven*. The last ship to be handed over by the Dockyard was the *Clan Ross* in 1965.

With this move, Scotts' now had a complete shipyard from Cartsburn to Cartsdyke East. And in line with recommendations of the Geddes Report Scotts' merged with Lithgow of Port Glasgow in 1969.

Chapter 3

On the Stocks

Over the years the yards were fairly stringent on the matter of time-keeping, although the hours and regulations varied somewhat. At the Dockyard in the 1930s the day normally began with the blast of the yard hooter at 8.00 a.m. If the worker had not 'clocked-on' by 8.15 his wages were 'quartered' which meant the deduction of fifteen minutes pay. Late-comers would find the gate shut and immediate access to the yard impossible. On Friday nights the men were paid with coins wrapped in pound notes enclosed by an elastic band. The wages were not even put in a sealed envelope.

On Saturdays the men stopped work at 12.00 noon and by 2.00 p.m. many of them were off to Cappielow if the local senior team, Morton, had a home game. The Saturday afternoon football match was a traditional pastime for workers in general.

The winter scene in the Cartsdyke yard towards the end of the 1930s was quite atmospheric with arc lighting extensively used on account of the short daylight hours, the noise of riveting, the incessant tapping of caulking hammers and the yard working to full capacity with all three berths occupied. In winter, too, machines often had to be heated by wood fires to prevent the hydraulics freezing. The winters were dry and cold in those days but the men worked hard and kept warm.

In the 1950s a very obvious difference between Scotts' and the Dockyard was noted in the 'clocking-on' system. At Scotts' a flexible arrangement operated whereby the workers had fifteen minutes to 'clock-on' between 7.40 and 7.55 a.m. The fifteen minutes gave most men the chance to get into the yard by 7.55 and then the men would go immediately to their workplace without any loitering or distraction. At 'Klondyke' in the early 1950s the gates were shut at 7.40 but even if men were in the yard by then, time was often wasted before they drifted off to their work. Generally punctuality was deplorable and there was further loss caused by squads being disrupted with men without mates. By 1955 this problem was overcome with managers and foremen seeing the men on to the ships immediately after the start.

The five and a half day week was still common at that time. Christmas Day working ensured that men would endure pangs of regret at missing festivities with the family. Of course, these arrangements were not peculiar to shipyards and were fairly widespread throughout Scotland.

However, many time-keepers turned a 'blind eye' towards men who might arrive at work shortly after the horn had stopped. But in the 1950s there was for a spell a real martinet at Cartsburn who was known not merely to refuse latecomers entry but to shut the gate in the face of men only seconds late. He would not admit them for fifteen minutes and of course they were then subjected to the 'quartering' penalty. He did the same in the afternoon and his reputation acquired such widespread notoriety that it was even rumoured his name was scrawled with unmentionable graffiti in public toilets as far flung as Sydney, Australia.

By 1970 'clocking-on' had not changed significantly. Workers living within sight of the clock-tower at Scotts' had no difficulty in getting to work for the 7.40 start. They would also be alerted by the horn going at 7.35, 7.40 and 7.45. The 'quartering' fine was still in force and if time-keeping was bad, e.g. three times in succession, latecomers would be turned away. But there must be sympathy for workers who lived further afield and came in by bus from such outlying places as Braeside. Bad winter weather in those higher-up spots could affect public transport and delay workers but they were still subject to regulations. Many workers of the older generation and conditioned by an earlier start to the day were often in the yard as early as 6.30 a.m., generally getting prepared for their day-lighting braziers in winter, brewing tea and getting their tools ready.

I reflected on the generations of men who had worked, laughed, cried and even died in these yards. And what a great range of occupations and skills there were:– yard managers, under-managers, foremen, cabinet-makers, caulkers, riggers, platers, riveters, holders-on, cranemen and shipwrights. The shipwright was involved in every stage of building ships from the beginning of the gestation period through to trials and his was a trade which went back to Elizabethan times.

The setting of the keel blocks required great precision and they were usually moved into position on to the berth by crane; a rope or hawser slipped easily through a hole just below the flat top of these concrete blocks whose dimensions varied. Occasionally they were shifted, surprisingly easily, by a wooden platform on rollers which were made up of welders' rods or pipes.

The blocks had to follow a straight line, with the correct height fore and aft having been calculated previously. The keel-laying could only take place after layers of wood were placed on top of the blocks, the final layer being made up of the 'capping pieces'.

The accuracy of the block positions was tested by a series of sights and a light filament from a 100-watt lamp. The check was usually done at night, it being more difficult to see the light clearly during daylight. The sights were placed at intermediate distances along the full length of the blocks and sometimes there was a false reading when the light reflected on the blocks. Indeed, sometimes there was no reading at all when workers accidentally hung their jackets over one of the sights.

The completed job required the foreman's approval and if he spotted even a minor error it had to be corrected. The foreman had tremendous authority in the yard and a worker dared not ignore his bidding or query his decision, even if the judgement was open to question.

Sometimes members of the squad laying the keel blocks were themselves aware of a small inaccuracy but did not think it serious enough to merit reconstruction. It was possible for them to 'con' the foreman by 'flogging' the sights and distract his attention from the flaw by getting him to avoid looking through a sight near the mistake.

Shipyard fires were not uncommon and in 1977 a night fire destroyed about sixty yards of keel blocks and launch ways at Cartsdyke. The blaze, which was discovered by the gateman at 2.30 a.m., affected the keel blocks beneath the second drill ship under construction in the yard. The *Pacnorse I* was due to be launched several weeks later.

After the keel blocks were positioned the uprights were erected. These slender metal girders had been a regular feature of my early doodles of ships on the stocks but it was only recently that I learned their name and something about their purpose. As many as twenty uprights rose up in parallel lines on the berth, stretching as high as seventy feet, with the distance between the lines fixed by the breadth of the designed hull. There was usually an added allowance of several feet on either side. Each upright was bolted to a flat metal base connected to a large stone block which was firmly sunk in a deep hole.

A worker once was securing shores towards the stern of a ship under construction. As the tide was in, he was wearing waders but unfortunately he stepped into a vacant upright hole, three feet under the water, and almost disappeared from view. There was great merriment at his misfortune.

The uprights were approximately aligned at right angles to the ground and while unconnected and in isolation they swayed alarmingly in strong winds, making life difficult for anyone working aloft.

In the 1950s a squad working on the main deck of a ship at Cartsdyke were being constantly hounded by a particularly vigilant foreman who made it difficult for the men to get on with their work. He appeared out of the blue on deck, and then popped up again at a totally different spot. He achieved this type of surveillance by scuttling up and down the uprights.

There were foremen who sacked men at the blink of an eye and they often kept order with their fists. One foreman, a formidable ex-featherweight boxer, made a habit of climbing over the back gate of the Dockyard to take the night shift by surprise and woe betide anyone who was slacking on the job.

For many years, in the yards, there was no official tea-break permitted but men did not follow this ruling and furtive brew-ups were always on the go. With plenty of fires and furnaces always burning there was never a shortage of boiling water and the tea was often accompanied by toast or fried bread. Foremen and managers were constantly on the prowl and the tin tea cans were hastily abandoned on the deck or the ground if bosses were in the vicinity. As the bosses passed they simply kicked over the cans while the workforce sullenly got on with their jobs. Workers found this practice quite irksome and one squad of welders plotted revenge on a bullying foreman who soon was to acquire the nickname 'Hopalong Cassidy', after taking a swipe, with his boot, at a large can which had been deliberately welded to the deck. I suppose the managers were only doing their job and it was estimated that as much as thirty minutes, morning and afternoon, could be wasted in tea-breaks.

It was traditional to have tea cans in the shipyard while the fitting-out trades carried thermos flasks, most notably the joiners.

As the building of the ship began, the uprights were linked by wood bracers and wire. Steel thwarts were fixed, jutting inwards towards the hull; the scaffolding was completed by laying stage planking on the thwarts.

The workforce had a traditional respect for the 'stagers' who erected this structure. It could rise to a considerable height and, although the stagers were on a bonus to finish the job as quickly as possible, the hazards especially in winter were considerable. The staging, which was yellow-painted by the 1970s, soon became known as the 'yellow peril'.

Accidents were frequent and, for example, in the early 1930s a plater who was working at the stern of a ship at Cartsburn plunged thirty-five feet when the plank on which he was standing slipped off the thwart. He died almost immediately from a fractured skull.

After setting the uprights shipwrights could go on to keel-laying, fitting bottom frames, side frames and outside hull plates.

At Cartsburn in the 1950s as many as 200 men were employed on basic hull construction, divided into squads working fore, aft, amidships and probably on piece-work. Each squad consisted of one charge-hand, three men, a boy and one labourer. At Klondyke piece-work was limited and only about eighty worked on a ship at one time. Piece-work applied there only to riveters and welders, outfit squads and sometimes contract platers.

One of the standard shipwright tools was the 'maul', a versatile type of hammer the size of which could be tailored to an individual's require-

A keel section being positioned on the berth at Cartsburn in 1961. Uprights have already been erected on either side of the slip.

ments. The men usually had their own tools and it was a measure of the trust to be found in the local yards in the 1950s when a tradesman at Cartsburn, who was off work for about a fortnight through illness, returned to find his tools in the exact spot on deck where he had left them.

Construction materials, supplied often by crane, were all fed to the area where each squad was working and left in the correct place for easy access. There were never swarms of men seen to be working at one time; large numbers would only have made more demands on the limited crane facilities and the smooth-flowing distribution and utilisation of parts would be interrupted.

There were conflicting reports about the methods of plate assembly in both yards in the 1950s. At Cartsburn it was said that frames and plates were pulled into their correct position by 'horning' wires from inside the hull. Extensive lengths of completed hull plating were then checked by the eagle-eyed foreman who 'eyeing-up' saw at a glance if a plate was misaligned. If this was the case he asked for it to be reset. There were rumours at Klondyke of occasions when hammering and riveting replaced more subtle methods of realigning plates. However, Scotts' work was influenced by Admiralty standards; Dockyard ships were 'faired' to best merchant ship practice and the Clan Line had a hull inspector who worked closely with the foremen and would not have accepted anything less.

Since the development of the iron and steel ship, the work of the plater has been of great importance in the shipyard. A Cartsdyke shipyard worker received great local press coverage in 1957, having acquired the reputation as the world's oldest plater. Tom Kerrigan, better known as 'Tam', who was aged eighty-nine, had spent over seventy-six years in the yards, at first as a template boy at Klondyke which he called the 'wee yerd.' Templates then were lifted from the ship on the berth and the plates were cut to shape by shears. A photograph in the paper showed Tam shearing a large steel plate measuring twenty feet by five feet and weighing about a ton. Beforehand hundreds of rivet holes had been punched through the plate which was soon to be an integral part of yet another Clan liner. Tam's secret was[1] 'early to bed, early to rise' and he got up 'fresh as paint at 6.00 a.m. ready for the starting whistle.' Although shearing was a precise job, Tam did not wear special glasses to get a correct cut. He enjoyed a dram after work and indicated that 'a glass of whisky warms the cockles of the heart but it must not interfere with work.' He enjoyed

---

[1] *Greenock Telegraph.*

his work so much that even at eighty-nine he was not contemplating retirement. Thirty years ago employers often retained workers beyond normal retirement age; it saved the expense of training a new apprentice and companies were not willing to lose a highly-skilled worker.

Some two years later Tam, at the age of ninety-one, was presented with the B.E.M. on the launching platform, two hours before the *Rotherwick Castle* went into the water. The medal was awarded in the Birthday Honours of June 1959; Tam's retirement came in October of that year.

One of the shipyard managers knew Tam well. He collected his wages on a Friday night, headed for his local pub and put money on the counter as advance payment for the following week's consumption, which was precisely two halfs of whisky after work each night. His daughter was most unhappy at his continued employment at the multiple-punch machine after he had reached the age of eighty and on several occasions pleaded with the Dockyard management to pay him off.

Working conditions inside the evolving hull were most unpleasant, with one of the most awkward areas known as the 'coffin plate' at the lower after end where it was exceptionally claustrophobic.

A former sheet metal worker described the tough conditions during the building of the Australian and Chilean submarines in the early 1970s at Cartsburn. The design of these conventional submarines was based on the British 'Oberon' class. Inside the hull there was limited room for manoeuvre and Joe recalled the restricted space when working with two others in a tank some six feet long; he constantly banged his head in the cluttered lower-deck area where the lack of air, the smell, the dirt and pungent fumes were almost overpowering; hold-ups and delays were a constant problem and on one occasion he spent several hours in a torpedo hatch awaiting a plumber before he could continue with his fitting.

There was no-one in authority at that time approaching the Cartsdyke 'Eye Specialist', a bossy and arrogant manager, of the immediate postwar period, who was always on the prowl and lectured frequently about how 'I did this . . . and I did that . . .' – referring to a previous employment. But programmes had to be met and the workforce was under pressure not to fall behind. There were regular inspections by navy specialists and all naval and merchant ships from the mid-1950s were taken at competitive fixed prices and production rates had to be maintained.

There was an explosion on board the Chilean submarine *Hyatt* while she was fitting-out at Cartsburn in 1976. The blast was in the forward engine room of the submarine and happened just after the squad working there had returned from lunch. All seven men were rescued, with one being badly burned. At the time it was believed that the accident was caused by a leakage of propane gas from a fractured blow torch pipe.

The sections of these submarines and merchant ships at Cartsburn were assembled in the prefabrication shed, where electrically-powered over-head cranes did the lifting work. The largest crane was over sixty feet high and the 'Big Hook' of this imposing machine was capable of taking a load of twenty tons and the 'Small Hook', five tons. The 'Small Hook' behaved like a whippet and great care had to be exercised by the craneman as it lifted much quicker than expected and responded to the controls with great sensitivity. The crane performed a great range of tasks and the most common was to unload plates, newly arrived from the adjacent plate shop, pile them up and finally distribute them according to the instructions of the platers. Many plates were deposited by the massive roller machines to be prepared finally for completion as bulkheads. The roller squad also helped shape the hull plates for the outer skin of the ship's hull. Oil had dripped from the tank of the roller machine for many years, though in the winter the drip was less frequent. However, it could seldom be heard and indeed there were days when the men could not hear each other speak without shouting into ears and even then it was difficult to interpret what was being said. In the early 1970s there was still plenty of work in the yards and with the constant noise and activity both day and night the shed became known as 'The Jungle'. Productivity requirements were high and consequently the hardest foremen, the best managers and arguably the finest tradesmen were to be found there.

Sometimes the plates would have to be laid out by the crane as the start for building a unit. This involved very intricate crane work as the plates had to be dropped on to a chalk line and laid out in a kind of pattern with each plate numbered and in its correct place.

Although its safe lifting load was twenty tons the crane often lifted double that weight. In tandem with another similar crane the overhead, if required, could lift a prefabricated section of up to eighty tons on to a low bogey for transportation to the berth outside. These completed units were described as 'Lego Cathedrals' by the workforce. When the units were on the move the large doors of the shed were opened and even in the middle of summer it could be very cold inside the building. But the men did not complain as the draught took away the welding fumes and the smoke from the burning machines.

The crane was serviced monthly, with particular attention paid to oiling and greasing the wheels and cog-wheels at the cabin end. Such a regular overhaul was probably unnecessary but it kept the crane in good, constant working order. A day or two after the service 'she' became easier to handle and ran smoother and faster over the rails; again the operator had to be particularly alert. The nippled cat-walk was also swept regularly and all rubbish removed in case it fell on the workers below.

One operator made conditions as cosy as possible in his cab; in winter he had an electric fire and bedding; during spells of inactivity he wrote poetry and read books. At the tea-break he lifted the crane-hook to allow the crane to move slowly into its platform and climbed down the ladder. On the ground he had a cigarette, toast or roll and drank tea from a black can before ascending the ladder again. His workmates often showed concern about the isolation of the operator cocooned in his cab. Cats were always sniffing about the shed, searching out haversacks containing pieces or other food and the men tossed the dregs of their tea at them; the workers did not like the smell of cats either.

Occasionally the operator lost control when the crane was overloaded and a plate being lowered gently, suddenly accelerated and crashed to the floor.

Accidents were frequent, although generally of a minor nature. Quite often fingers were nipped or crushed by plates and workers on the floor had to be ever aware of crane movements. However, in the early 1970s a circular rib cage section of a submarine fell from the supporting sling, bumped off several jobs on the floor and finally came to rest, trapping a young worker. The inner part of the unit had an edge like a razor and, as the man was held in a vice-like grip, thick black blood spurted from a deep gash in his leg.

By the 1970s welders attracted a great deal of sympathy, especially when working with galvanised plate. The inhalation of fine dust particles caused the welder to shake as though he had malaria and some welders suffered from a condition known as 'welder's lung', similar to emphysema, which was contracted more quickly if the welder was working in the narrow confines of a submarine hull. If possible, extraction ventilation was provided. There were the 'unsung heroes' – the Red Leaders who had to endure the noxious fumes as they painted the hull. This was especially nasty in the pre-mask days when noses and mouths were covered with a handkerchief, a futile protective gesture. Boiler scalers and insulation squads putting in lagging were also affected by working in restricted spaces.

Accidents were commonplace in the environment of the yards. During the construction of the gearless bulk carrier *Clydesdale*, and only some weeks before her launch at Scotts' in June 1967, there was a fatality when a man was burned to death. This happened as the engineer was working with a welder and two other men in a tank on the ship. There was no warning at all as sparks from the welder's torch caused his clothes to catch fire and, although his workmates quickly carried him from the tank, he died shortly after his arrival in hospital. When the death was announced 170 men employed in the outside engineering department stopped work out of sympathy.

Some years later a plater was killed by a propeller as it was being fitted and again onlookers experienced the eerie atmosphere as the platers shuffled to the main gate on hearing the news.

Incidentally the *Clydesdale* was the largest ship built at Scotts' although only marginally bigger than two similar vessels built subsequently for a Greek owner. The *Clydesdale* had a deadweight tonnage of 41,500 and the Greek-owned ships a deadweight of 41,450.

In the nineteenth and early twentieth centuries most iron and steel ships were assembled by hand-riveting; the rivet was a short length of iron or

Greenock & Grangemouth Dockyard platers, 1913. A trades pose was a common feature of shipyard life.

The launch of the Clydesdale, *the largest ship built by Scotts', 1967.*

steel rod with a head, up to five inches long, depending on the thickness of
the plate. The rivet squad, a very close-knit unit, consisted of four men –
two riveters, a 'hauder up' or 'hauder on' and a 'rivet boy' or 'catch boy'.
A young man who started as an apprentice in the Dockyard in 1953 was
astounded to see that the 'catch boy' in one rivet squad was over sixty-five
and had a long white beard; the 'boy' in many instances was often as old
as fifty.

The rivet, heated to red heat for several minutes in a portable pan with
the assistance of bellows, was extracted from the hearth by a 'heater boy'
armed with a long pair of tongs. The rivet was then tossed to the 'catch
boy' who grabbed it skilfully with his tongs; a rivet was too hot to handle
even with gloved hands. The 'catch boy' put the rivet through a punched
hole in the overlapping plates. Then the 'hauder on' held up a very heavy
hammer to the underside of the rivet head while the riveter hammered and
flattened it into the hole. They also hammered over the end of the rod and
made a second head. The hammer used by the riveters was fairly light and
weighed only five pounds; skill and technique were much more important
than pure strength. With the advent of aluminium rivets it was important
to avoid too much heat, which caused the rivets to become brittle so that

they broke easily. To prevent this happening, sand was added to the rivet pan and this kept the temperature to a safe level.

In the early days of hand-riveting, hot rivets were often deliberately dropped from the deck of a ship under construction on to the bare heads of disliked managers walking below. It was rumoured that, as a consequence, they took to wearing, for protective purposes, reinforced bowler hats which soon became a familiar sight in shipyards to the present day. Former staff, though, have pointed out that managers originally wore hats as a badge of office. They took to wearing bowlers which had a life expectancy three or four times that of a soft hat.

Many years ago there was often a major ceremony at a keel-laying, usually of warships, with dignatories, yard officials and workers present as the closure of the first rivet was made; it was then that the first payment to the builder was made.

Joe also worked on the *Fort Grange*, the first of two large replenishment ships built for the Royal Fleet Auxiliary. What impressed him was the vast area of the engine room cavity, before the machinery was installed. On one occasion, there, a copper smith working at the bottom sustained a severe head injury after he was struck by a spanner, dropped from above, and knocked out.

At Greenock Dockyard in 1959, a plumber who was working at the foot of a hold suddenly looked up to see a man hurtling towards him. The riveter landed on a tank top at the bottom of a ladder and bounced about twelve inches before coming to rest. He died almost immediately from multiple injuries which included fractures of the skull and thigh; the Fatal Accidents Inquiry concluded that he might have fallen between twenty-five and thirty-eight feet.

In the 1930s at Cartsdyke, there was an accident which curiously did not involve a death or injury. A former worker recalled that from ground level he had looked up at the bare skeleton of a hull under construction on the berth. To his horror he saw, at a height of some thirty feet, a boy actually running, somewhat precariously, along a steel beam some three inches wide. Not surprisingly, he slipped and fell to the ground. A stretcher was immediately called for and workers feared the worst but the boy slowly struggled to his feet, having escaped with nothing more than a severe winding. Incidentally, the Dockyard had a good reputation for finding lighter employment for a worker returning after serious injury had affected his health.

Laymen often made sneering comments about the cushy work, indolence and lethargic atmosphere in the shipyard. An employee of Scotts' in the early 1960s responded by inviting a particularly scathing critic to spend part of a day watching him at his work. The sceptic was smuggled into the yard and was fortunate to escape the formidable vigilance of management, foremen and security staff. It was winter and the visitor spent a miserable few hours observing from an exposed position on the poop deck. As he cowered behind a deck house, sleet and thunderstorms accompanied by a biting wind swept across the deck from the north, doubts were soon allayed. He was lucky; he could have been entertained at George Brown's yard located at Garvel Point, Greenock, and known locally as 'Siberia.'

By the early years of the twentieth century, hydraulic and pneumatic riveting were introduced, which to a great extent replaced hand-riveting. On larger shell or deck plates, powered methods were more efficient but, on light work involving small, closely-spaced rivets, hand riveters could keep up a good rate of 200 rivets per day. In fact, from 1926 there was a wage reduction of twenty-six per cent for power riveters. Automation also resulted in the rivet squads being cut in numbers and latterly comprised only three men – a riveter, a 'hauder-on' and a 'rivet boy'.

Before the invention of shot-blasting and prefabrication, stern plates were left by the water's edge below high-water mark and covered by the incoming tide. The salt water and outdoor weathering speeded up the rusting process which was necessary to remove all traces of 'mill scale'.

When Greenock Dockyard started prefabrication, the shell-plates had been shot-blasted and primed previously at the steel works. Stern units were already painted in hull colours with name and port of registry and the only time they were put near the water was when there was no other space available. The few times sections were caught by the tide, it was an exceptionally high tide.

Before the Dockyard introduced welding, pails of salt water were often thrown over deck rivets to rust them up and ensure a tighter deck. It was also said that workers relieved themselves over the deck rivets and this had a similar effect to that of salt water.

In the 1950s there was a well-known rivet squad involved in piece-work at Cartsdyke. The team often climbed into the yard, when it was closed on a Saturday afternoon and Sunday morning, and of course got off to a flying start on the Monday morning.

A Mr. McGhee, Houlder Brothers' steel inspector and a former riveter to trade, was involved in the supervision of that company's cargo liner *Swan River* building at Greenock Dockyard in 1959. He was extremely critical about the rivet points finish, which was not up to the standard he

A fifty-six-ton stern section being fitted to the Falaba *at Scotts' in 1961. Her sister ship* Fourah Bay *is at a more advanced stage of construction in the next berth. These two cargo liners were building for Elder Dempster.*

had been accustomed to in his shipyard days. The completed work of the Dockyard riveters had always satisfied the Clan Line inspectors and met the requirements of Lloyd's who had no complaints about the *Swan River*. McGhee's frequent grievances about the supposed poor quality of their work annoyed the riveters to the extent that they chalked in large lettering the name *Clan McGhee* high up on either side of the unpainted bow of the *Swan River* while she was still on the stocks. The inspector was not amused as this sight confronted him on entering the yard the following morning. Apparently McGhee was also presented with a number of faulty 'dog leg' rivets which had been removed by Dockyard workers from plates of a ship under repair in the nearby Garvel Dry Dock. This vessel had been built at a yard in the north-east of England at a time when McGhee was foreman riveter there.

Riveting continued at the Dockyard until 1960 but after then was carried out in tandem with welding, the process whereby steel was joined by using electric current which caused plates to join at the edge and become bonded. The caulker then trimmed off the steel after it had been welded.

As the ship gradually took shape, timber bilge blocks and shores gave support to the bottom and sides of the hull. In 1957 a worker was injured

Riveting and welding going on simultaneously at Scotts', 1948.

when shoring up the keel of a ship with a hydraulic jack one night at Scotts'. The staging block slipped, struck him and he was later detained in the Royal Infirmary with a suspected fractured skull.

Some of this wood was often dislodged by a high tide or adverse weather conditions. At Lamont's, Port Glasgow, in 1957 a fourteen-foot-long carpenter's dingy, with several men on board including a rigger's mate and foreman carpenter, had gone out from the yard to collect shoring timber and keel ends swept into the River by a flood tide. The boat was unable to get back and the men, who had been operating inshore, were spotted and shipyard workers raised the alarm. A launch was sent out to their assistance from Princes Pier, Greenock. The dingy was lashed by a southwesterly gale and as the occupants fought to control the boat in the heavy seas it was carried further into the shipping channel. The men, who were drenched by waves, kept afloat by continuous baling and eventually reached a buoy where they tied up until the launch arrived to rescue them.

Former workers recalled the early 1950s at 'Klondyke' where there was general congestion with the three berths in operation. The old-fashioned and quite primitive 'pole' derricks which serviced the berths had their origins at the beginning of the century, but some shipyards had since replaced them with tower cranes. But, although these derricks only carried light loads, their efficiency and ease of operation were most impressive. They were worked quite often by one man who was able to obtain what material he required without any delay.

Some workers sneered at the four new cranes assembled at Cartsdyke in 1958. Butters were not well-known locally as crane-makers and to many of the workers the design was unorthodox and bore little resemblance to their more conventional Cartsburn neighbours which were generally of the tower design and made by Arrol. However, in general the labour force was delighted to have modern cranes. The four pyramid-shaped travelling cranes with their lengthy jibs handled crane-lifts much better than the hammer-heads in Scotts'. Most lifts in Greenock Dockyard at that time were under twenty tons but two cranes operating in unison coped adequately with a lift of fifty tons. Had the Dockyard continued independently these cranes would have been replaced with sixty or eighty tonners of the same type.

In 1957 shortly before the new cranes went up, an electrician fell to his death from the gantry of one of the Cartsdyke five-ton cranes.

The new mobile cranes were erected on top of two substantial concrete ramps beside the berth to give a level, elevated runway. Under the west crane ramp, towards the seaward end, was a store used for keeping shores and other bits of wood. There were stories of this being an improvised bothy which evolved into a 'hawff' acquiring the name 'Ponderosa'. The occasional flooding at high tide forced the occupants to effect a rapid retreat. Apparently in the same refuge a small gas burner was kept, on which tea was brewed and mince and cabbage cooked for 'pieces'.

There were memories too of the Klondyke sawmill, the roof of which was blown off in a severe winter gale in the 1950s but was not replaced for several days. In the meantime the labour force struggled on amid freezing conditions which were not improved by the totally ineffective gas heaters.

A long-term problem at Scotts' came to a head in 1959 when complaints were made by the yard to Greenock Corporation about the town's sewage disposal system. Employees engaged in fitting-out were sickened by the stench of raw sewage which flowed into the Basin. The problem was aggravated with the constant presence of flocks of scavenging seagulls. There were eighteen places within the Burgh boundary with sewage outfalls in the Clyde. One of these was in Scotts' fitting-out Basin and another in the middle of the yard. Scotts' concern was that one of the sewers had a broken pipe and that both caused a nuisance. The yard wanted the matter dealt with as soon as possible.

A former Dockyard employee, a third-year apprentice draughtsman in 1942, recalled the primitive toilet situation which incidentally was common to many other shipyards at that time. The 'W.C.' was located by the water, adjacent to a barbed-wire perimeter fence which marked the boundary with Scotts'. This facility was placed as conveniently as possible to the berths, saving time being wasted through men making a long trudge to the rear of the yard. However, this concession was ignored by many men who chose to squat inside the hull shell. The 'W.C.', known as the 'Long Drop', consisted of a series of wee cubicles on wooden staging which was supported by stilts; below the staging was a metal trough with running water. This provision was not to be abused, with five minutes the maximum permitted visiting time. The trough, which assisted the removal of waste products, ran along the full length of the 'building' and also provided a great source of amusement for practical jokers who often set fire to screwed-up balls of paper, despatched them down the water course and awaited the cries of pain and shock as bare bottoms were briefly roasted by the burning paper sailing underneath. This practice was widespread in Clyde shipyards, which had similar facilities at the time.

In the course of World War II, the Dockyard labour force reacted in astonishment and disbelief to the startling news that Hamilton's of Port Glasgow had installed a flushing toilet system.

After World War I and the defeat of Germany there was a popular cry in Britain to 'Hang the Kaiser!' In the 1920s Klondyke sanitation facilities had acquired such notoriety that this demand was amended to 'Hang the Cayzer' – a reference to the new owning family.

Significant improvements in the early 1950s resulted in the replacement of the trough by 'W.C.' pans in the cubicles which were connected to an outside flushing system. But there was misuse with seats broken or stolen. The first new toilet, with tiled walls, was opened in 1959 on the south side of the main road and was followed in 1962 by another similar standard toilet at the head of the berths. Both had attendants to keep them clean and were fitted with wash hand basins. Shop stewards gave undertakings that there would be no vandalism and kept their word. Also in 1962 a changing room with showers was opened.

Although Scotts' built new 'W.C.'s and dismantled old ones when the welding bay was built in 1954, the facilities were generally inadequate until the 1960s. There was no privacy in the 'W.C.'s, housed in a corrugated hut where the occupants had to sit on thick planks similar to railway sleepers with a large hole cut in the centre. Waste was removed via a narrow, open sewer with a stream of running water which ran beneath the shed.

Despite the criticism, the yards' sanitation probably compared favourably with that in such places as football grounds and railway stations.

The old drawing offices at the Dockyard used to be just above the main gate and once a day the peaceful atmosphere in the building was shattered as the light locomotive passed underneath. The engine, which shunted wagons with steel plates and sections, caused the building to vibrate and stour to rise; fumes belched from the chimney and polluted the air.

For some years after World War II Scotts' was served by the ubiquitous CARTSBURN No. 2. This steam locomotive was mainly engaged in shunting work within the yard complex but also carried plates to the yard from the foundry. If foremen shipwrights happened to be in their shed by the fitting-out basin in the late afternoon, they were often distracted by the sound of the engine puffing slowly past with the accompanying cry from the driver announcing, 'The 4.15 to Cartsdyke!' Actually there was no rail link between Cartsburn and Cartsdyke but any journey on that locomotive would have been a bone-shattering experience.

The railway tracks were a constant hazard for cyclists, especially in wet and greasy conditions and riders were thrown off their machines when the wheels became stuck in the grooves.

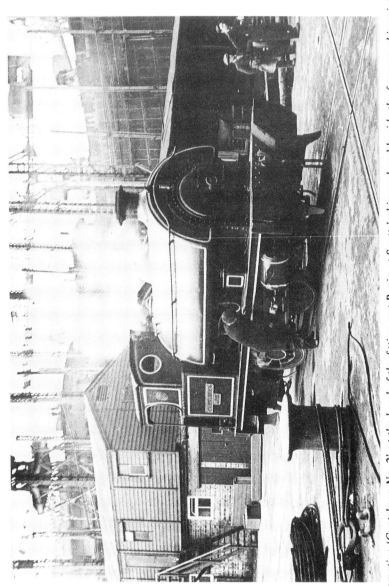

Locomotive 'Cartsburn No. 2' at the head of the fitting-out Basin at Scotts' shipyard and beside the foremen shipwrights' shed, 1948.

Chapter 4

Characters

Characters of all types filled the yards over the years. These included the Scotts' worker known as 'Crazy Horse' who reacted violently on seeing someone smoking in his vicinity. A discarded cigarette end on the ground also provoked wild behaviour as he imagined that to be a poisonous snake.

Tommy Hendry, a very popular workmate, was held in such high regard by his fellows that he soon became known as 'King Henry'. One day he was greeted with astonishment by one of his colleagues who exclaimed, 'I thought you were dead!' Tommy lightly dismissed this by replying, 'But that was the other king!' King George VI had died the day before.

A foreman renowned for his sartorial elegance at work, was known as 'The Duke'. He always dressed immaculately with one of his choicest garments worn at work being a velvet jacket.

There was a plater at Cartsburn whose main interests were canary breeding, boxing and mountain climbing. He kept over thirty birds in a large aviary in his back garden and had achieved great success with the birds at numerous meetings and shows. He had started boxing in fairground booths and finally reached Scottish selection.

A welder at Scotts' was nicknamed 'The Burd' owing to his keen interest in playing the saxophone. His name was derived from Charlie 'Yardbird' Parker, the great jazz musician.

The temporary lighting man who worked at Cartsburn for over thirty years had had quite a chequered career, before he went into shipbuilding, as a variety artiste and an opera singer, appearing in London, Manchester, Belfast and Dublin. After he retired in 1983 his plans for the future included making a movie film of Greenock.

'Big Tex' who had worked in Scotts' for twenty-four years was committed to introduce elements of the nineteenth-century Wild West to

Scotland. For some time he was organiser of The Lone Star Country and Western section of the Scott Lithgow club and his major aim was to hold an open championship organised by the Scottish League of Gunfighters to find the fastest draw in Scotland.

It was traditional to have lots of cats prowling about the yard and in 1973 a Cartsburn worker had problems with a particularly vicious animal which frequently went for him. Unable to tolerate the situation any longer, the welder got a bag, put a heavy weight inside, snatched up the offending creature with welder's gloves and popped it into the sack which he then threw into Scotts' Basin.

Drinking had for long been a notorious feature of the shipyard worker's life. As far back as 1890 there was a local report of the Boilermakers' and Iron Shipbuilders' Union expressing their regret 'that the abominable vice of intemperance still continues to work dreadful havoc amongst some of our men.'[1]

In the late 1950s there was a rivet squad who acquired a reputation for ensconsing themselves, immediately after work on a Friday, in the Para Handy pub opposite the Dockyard. The senior member of the squad came in with the collective wages, placed them on the counter and the squad then proceeded to drink away a good proportion of their week's earnings. Their approach was by no means unique and it was no surprise that Mr. Swan, the then Secretary and Director of the Dockyard and a teetotaller, grumbled about that hostelry as being the 'Too Handy'. The common poke method of paying the rivet squad went out shortly after the advent of P.A.Y.E. when each man's earnings had to be accounted for. The licensee of the Para Handy one year accepted holiday credit vouchers to clear the slate for a number of clients. He called on Mr. Swan to negotiate payment of the vouchers and left a worried man on being informed that the vouchers were non-transferable and the money had to be collected by the man to whom the voucher belonged.

It was also quite common for men to apply for an early pay on Friday afternoons. This ensured an early exit to avoid meeting the money lender or a wife or ex-wife who wanted to get some of the money before most of it was spent on drink.

There was much more labour movement between the Greenock yards after their merger in 1966 and later amalgamation with Lithgow in 1970. From that period a character by the name of 'Dracum', a yard carpenter, emerged. He had acquired a formidable reputation as a drinker and his

---

[1] *Greenock Telegraph.*

nickname was derived apparently from the old Scots word 'Dracht', meaning a measure of liquid. The story goes that late one Saturday night, in a drunken condition, he was making his way home from the pub. He lived in the top flat of a tenement building but on approaching the close discovered his house keys were missing. However, undaunted, he proceeded to gain entry by climbing up on a rone pipe, swinging over to his bedroom window ledge, opening the window and jumping inside. Mayhem resulted as he crawled into bed only to find the woman lying next to him was not his wife. He was in the wrong house.

It was reported that on another drunken occasion, while standing late at night on the platform of Port Glasgow station, he became involved in a minor scuffle with a stranger. He pushed his assailant down and suspecting that he might have rolled off the platform onto the track, ran off. The next day he mentioned the incident to some friends who later produced a *Sunday Post* which had a stop press entry that the police were looking for a man in connection with a body found at Port Glasgow station. When shown this, 'Dracum' went quite ashen and set off immediately to the police station to give himself up. But the police had no knowledge of the alleged murder and Dracum's friends had inserted the details of the crime in a blank stop press column.

There were further tales from the 1970s: a sheet metal worker was arrested one Saturday night for being 'Drunk and Incapable'. It was his third similar offence and, fearing a custodial sentence, he sought advice from his foreman who was also a Baillie. The predicament was described and the foreman listened sympathetically and gave assurances that, if he was on the bench that day, a fine would be the extent of the punishment. Fortunately the foreman was on duty at the trial and the accused smugly awaited the verdict with confidence. He was jailed for three months.

A labourer arrived for work at Cartsburn one Monday morning in a dehydrated condition and gasping for a drink. His workmates offered him what appeared to be red cola, which he gulped down. However, they had given him a light industrial oil and the victim required a stomach pump after being rushed to hospital.

Two burners working on a submarine at Scotts' were sacked for being drunk. They later returned to the yard, evaded security and proceeded to sabotage the submarine by attempting to burn holes through the hull.

An employee who had just received his two week 'Fair Holiday' wages of over £40 went directly to the betting shop and placed a bet of £36 on the favourite for a race. The horse lost and the unfortunate punter drank the remaining £4. He then put in his notice, resigned and picked up two weeks 'lying time'.

As the men left the yards at lunchtime and crossed the road, very few went to the pub and most made for the canteen. There were, however, exceptions. One lunchtime, after a few drinks, a Scotts' worker stole a jar of mint imperials from a local confectioner. He displayed a total lack of discretion in a generous distribution to workmates and the police soon apprehended the culprit. The local press reported the case with the headline 'Sweet tooth sheet-metal worker caught in action.'

There was the odd case of men drinking themselves into a stupor at lunchtime to the extent where they were carried back into the yard by workmates and left to sleep it off in ships' cabins until work ended for the day.

An outside crane-man at Klondyke had been celebrating something at lunchtime and, unusually for him, drank too much. He was spotted by the Head-Timekeeper who, knowing him to be a good man, refused to let him clock-in. A manager was called and pointed out to the inebriated man that in his condition he would fail a breathalyser. The drunken man retorted that he was not driving a car but a crane. He was not clocked-in and so escaped dismissal.

By the early 1970s there were productivity problems in the yards and many employees who had worked 'double-time' on Sunday had no inclination to appear on a Monday. There was a ten per cent bonus in pay packets on the Friday for those who had completed a full week's attendance.

There were occasions when workers were involved in activities unrelated to shipbuilding. In order to pick up I.T.V., when in its infancy in the mid-1950s, an aerial different from that receiving B.B.C. programmes was required. In Scotts' this problem was surmounted by the manufacture of an improvised copper aerial some six feet in length. Held close to the body, it was a relatively straightforward task to effect removal of this slim accessory from the yard.

A carpenter, employed at Scotts' in the 1950s, was shortly due to get married and his workmates decided to make an ornate dining room table as a wedding present. Much hard work went into the manufacture of this item of furniture with only the best quality wood being used. On completion, however, the obvious difficulty was how to sneak the table through the main gate. On the Friday night prior to the wedding, as the day's work ended, the groom-to-be was dressed up as was customary, and made to sit on top of the table which was lifted and then carried by the surrounding workmates. As the table was discreetly smuggled out of the yard the gate-keeper saw only a cheering, milling crown of young men apparently escorting and chairing a workmate through the exit.

All new apprentices had to undergo an initiation procedure when they were started in the yards and at Scotts' in the 1970s this usually involved a ritual ducking in the sink. One apprentice, who was much opposed to this practice, resisted all attempts to forcibly push his head under the water. He pleaded for mercy and his assailants backed off when he compromised, indicating a willingness to do it himself. As he prepared to immerse his head, a manager passing by paused to inquire what was going on. The young boy, who had heard already of the fearsome reputation attached to the managers, blurted out that he was merely washing his hair.

A new apprentice reporting for his first day at Scotts' in 1972, on a cold winter's morning, believed himself to be well-insulated against the cold by wearing a sweater and parka on top of his overalls. However, he was astonished to see men moving about the yard clad only in overalls. He discovered later that this was no act of genuine bravado as they had two sweaters underneath their boiler suits.

Chapter 5

Strikes

Shipyard strikes were a notorious feature of the 1950s and early 1960s on Clydeside. An old Scotts' worker recalled no all-out stoppages in the 1930s and 1940s, while one of his colleagues who retired in 1965 was proud to admit he had not been on strike since 1921. But strikes involving individual trades were quite common and productivity was badly affected. In 1958, fifty-two sheet-iron workers at Scotts' foundry went on strike for only a few days but it did delay the completion of the *Daru* whose trials had to be postponed. A local strike in 1960 involved only shipwrights and burners but lasted some five weeks and resulted in Greenock Dockyard actually having to close down for much of the duration. All steel work was suspended, although outfitting continued.

Many potential disputes at Scotts' and the Dockyard were prevented at weekends when managers would wander about the relatively quiet yard and pause to have informal chats with individual workers. These conversations often revealed a niggling problem which could then be solved amicably without having recourse to the unions.

In March 1957, on the Lower Reaches, there was a strike which involved all the shipyard unions; this was the first time in more than thirty years that all trades withdrew their labour. The Greenock yards were directly affected and the Dockyard postponed the launch of the *Clan Malcolm* which had been scheduled for the 15th April; a revised launch date was fixed after the strike was over. Refitting work on several Clyde steamers, being prepared for the summer season by local repair yards, was delayed. The Greenock Labour Exchange reported, at the time of the dispute, that the number of local men directly employed in the shipbuilding industry was 3,972. The local economy was also affected and at the beginning of the strike it was noted that the main streets of Greenock were unusually quiet, with the shopkeepers suffering an immediate loss of revenue. This in part was attributed to housewives anticipating hard times ahead when dependence on strike pay could bring in as little as twenty-eight shillings per week. As the strike progressed bakers lamented that, 'There was a decided falling off in the sales of fancies.'[1] The Greenock Co-operative Society Ltd, found, too, that sales slumped during the dispute and only noticed an improvement three weeks after the strike ended in early April. The dispute also had an impact on nearby resorts such as Rothesay, Millport, Dunoon, Largs and other Clyde Coast holiday towns. Spring was the time of year when inquiries were made about accommodation for the 'Fair' and landladies were concerned about a lack of interest in summer bookings.

But 1957 was a good year for the local yards, order books were healthy and payments at the start of the annual 'Fair' holiday fortnight were one of the biggest ever. There had been plenty of overtime and with considerable wage rises the ill effects of the strike were greatly reduced.

One day in November 1959, more than 600 men – the entire workforce – walked out of Greenock Dockyard. They had come out in sympathy because the management refused to reinstate a labourer dismissed for 'loafing'. The sacking took place as a result of an incident on board the *Rotherwick Castle* fitting-out in the James Watt Dock. In his defence the man was quoted as saying, 'There was no work for me to do and I had just taken a flask of tea from my pocket when a shipyard official walked up to me. I did not even have time to open my flask, so I wasn't drinking tea. After reporting to the foreman I was dismissed.[2]

The scene in the Greenock yards in the course of a strike is well described by the quote, 'An the boats'll no chynge that wee bit week by week, like they dae when ye're workin' . . . just stay the same . . . waitin' for ye tae come back tae finish them off.'[3]

Shortly after the strike in 1957 the employers and unions adopted one or two year 'No strike' agreements with the Boilermakers and these were renewed right up to nationalisation in 1977. On the union's side there were concessions on flexibility; for example, riveters were allowed to become tack welders and some, after a period of years, welders.

---

[1] *Greenock Telegraph.*

---

[2] *Greenock Telegraph.*

---

[3] Willie Rough.

Chapter 6

Launch

There has been a long tradition to hold most launches at a late morning or early afternoon high tide. This timing ensures a good depth of water and enables the post-launch lunch to be conveniently slotted in. In the 1920s and 1930s the thrifty management of money at the Dockyard was further demonstrated when workers were paid off immediately prior to the launch and then reinstated after the ship had entered the water. This system meant a saving for the yard of at least one hour's wages per man.

Although the launch of a ship seems to be a very straightforward and uneventful procedure, the preparation and build-up are quite complex. A former shipwright at Scotts' explained the mysteries of this operation. A few weeks before the launch, the 'standing ways' or fixed part of the launching slides were built-up on either side of the keel blocks. Concrete blocks formed the main base of these 'ways', blocks similar to those used for supporting the keel. Lengths of wood were then placed on top of these 'ways' which were also shored up. The 'ways' were then greased with tallow and black soap and the 'sliding ways' placed on top. With the danger of tallow freezing in winter, a precautionary fire was often lit under the ship. Occasionally a wooden 'sandwich' was inserted between the 'fixed' and 'sliding ways.' Incidentally, modern launching greases have an anti-freeze ingredient in the content.

The night prior to the launch, wooden wedges made of oak were hammered between the ship's hull and 'sliding ways' to effect a transfer of weight. These wedges were solid, had no 'give' and could be six or seven feet long; this procedure was referred to as 'ramming up'. During this operation the 'capping pieces' on top of the keel blocks were removed by 'splitting out' with the maul. These chunks of wood, made of Oregon pine, were easy to knock out as they had no knots and, while this was taking place, workmen began to dislodge the shores steadily from aft to fore. The last shores were removed only one hour before the launch.

'Poppets', a cradle of wood and metal built up to bow and stern, provided a cushion at these key spots subject to maximum stress as the ship entered the water. The wood on the cradle was joined together with bolts and rope while the metal part of the 'poppets' consisting of steel plate took the pressure off the wooden section.

It was a dramatic moment to see the vessel 'set up' the night before the launch and an even more exhilarating experience was to stand underneath the hull only hours before many thousands of tons of inert steel were transformed to life. The ship was free from support for the first time, restrained only by the launch 'triggers' or 'daggers' and at that moment of isolation there was never any question of doubt about the gender as 'she' creaked and groaned whilst sitting astride the 'sliding ways'.

Staging, of course, was also removed before the launch but even this task could be fraught with hazards: while dismantling staging before a launch at Scotts' in 1957, a carpenter's labourer was assisting in the removal of a thirty-five feet long plank by crane when the end of the plank bounced on the ground and struck him on the right forearm and right leg. He was detained in the R.I. for X-ray and examination.

Launches took place at the Dockyard without any water restrictions, owing to the alignment of the berths, but, although drag chains were not required, an ingenious system was implemented to arrest the momentum of a vessel after she had entered the water. A thick wire hawser was fixed adjacent to the starboard midships of a vessel on the ways and the end of the wire firmly attached to the ship. The hawser was shackled through an eye-plate which was bolted on to the hull with a great length of wire coiled alongside. The wire straightened out towards the stern and then stretched far into the channel, where it was connected to a 'drag' anchor sunk into the seabed and marked by a buoy. Before the launch a 'puffer' usually carried the anchor on the deck several hundred yards from the shore into the channel, where it was dropped to the bottom. The light tender *Torch* was often at hand to lift Light No. 14 from the navigation channel to prevent a possible obstruction to the launch. The *Torch* remained in attendance during the launch and replaced the light afterwards. Incidentally the *Torch* survived until 1977, when she was broken up at Dalmuir after fifty-two years of service. This attractive little vessel with her slim, buff funnel, straight stem and counter stern spent her career maintaining about 150 buoys extending from Erskine Bridge to Irvine Harbour.

As the new ship went down the ways, the hawser snaked out and when taut pulled the vessel up with the bow facing towards the east, to facilitate the manoeuvre into the James Watt Dock for fitting-out. On one or two occasions the Dockyard experimented with an alternative method, whereby plates were welded on to each side of the bow and acted as water brakes at the launch.

Most upriver yards dismantled all uprights before a launch to accommodate the piles of drag chains, but at the Dockyard most were left standing with only a few, on either side fore and aft, removed.

One of the final checks, carried out before the launch, was on the lower hull for missing rivets. If an empty hole was discovered, a tight-fitting wooden plug was hammered in and the affected spot shored up from the inside.

Sometimes on launch day the workers had their little joke, as befell the Clan Line superintendent at Cartsdyke when his name was chalked up on the bow of the *Clan Macinnes* in 1951.

Some ten minutes before the launch, bilge blocks were systematically knocked away, leaving the electrically-operated 'triggers' or 'daggers' fore and aft as the only constraints holding the ship in position on the slipway. The four 'daggers', bolted on to the side of the 'fixed ways', rested firmly against the cradle at bow and stern having been tested well in advance of launching. These were not always reliable and once at Cartsdyke the 'daggers' jammed at the crucial moment but the foreman in charge limited his frustration, annoyance and embarassment to a muted exclamation of, 'Oh, for God's Sake!' Usually, though, after the bottle smashed against the prow, the 'daggers' were released causing a sound similar to a bolt fired from a gun and the ship began to move.

Workers on deck shortly before the actual launch have described the ship as like a dog straining at the leash and others have felt a distinct 'creeping' before she started to go. It was an exhilarating experience as the 'light' hull gained momentum and clattered down the berth to an accompanying rattle and bang. Some ships would never go faster. A former Dockyard pilot recalled the freezing conditions on the bridge of a new ship in winter when the vessel, of course, was without heating. He also referred to Mrs. Hall, the official photographer, who was often to be seen high up on a crane recording the event.

For many years a great tradition of rivalry had existed between the Dockyard and Scotts'. At a given time, if Scotts' had a hull shell three-quarters complete and the Dockyard only a keel laid, the latter would be determined to catch up and get their ship launched first. It was especially

The launch of the World President *at Cartsdyke, 1969. Uprights, launching cradle and 'fixed ways' are clearly shown.*

prestigious to claim the first or the last launch of the year and, to achieve this target, corners often had to be cut. It was not obvious from the launching platform that parts of the superstructure were merely bolted together, that brown paper covered rivet holes in the superstructure and that the bridge front gleamed with whitewash. The red lead undercoat and gloss was applied later, after the whitewash was removed through vigorous wire-brushing by hand.

Although there was plenty of deep water at Greenock, tugs still had to move quickly into position to catch ropes thrown down to them from the deck. Several 'cod' ropes attached to the 'sliding ways' looped down from either side of the ship's hull; after the launch, these were tightened to pull in these ways from under the ship. Numerous small boats roamed around to pick up floating wood but it was difficult to recover all of this, as the effect of tide and current caused wood from launches to be washed up as far away as Dunoon and Largs.

The launch of the Clan Alpine, *the last Clan liner, at Scotts' Cartsdyke yard in 1967. Wood from the launch can also be seen clearly. The* Clan Alpine *was the name of the first Clan liner and also the last.*

During World War II a Sandbank joiner, experiencing a dearth of quality wood for his business, was able to obtain it, at a price, from an entrepreneur who worked on the local Hafton estate. East winds had driven the wood across the Clyde from the Greenock yards where it had been used for launches. And, of course, there was plenty as during hostilities yard productivity was at a high level and launches were frequent. As the flotsam drifted off the foreshore at Hafton, the estate employee made numerous boat sorties from the Hafton slip, retrieved the chunks of wood and soon built up a considerable stock which he had no difficulty in disposing of. Obviously during wartime the yards were not too meticulous in searching for their post-launch timber.

However, launches did not always run smoothly and sometimes 'poppets' were dislodged as the ship slid down the ways and wedges from the 'sliding ways' were ejected. If a high tide turned prematurely and there was not quite enough water at the crucial moment of entry, the ship bucked and reared as the stern smashed down on the water and the bow plunged down on to the ways; tallow was burned off and ways crushed into the ground with the pressure.

The Hafton shore looking towards the Holy Loch, 1990.

The Hafton shore, where much launch wood was washed up in World War II.
Looking towards Gourock and Greenock, 1990.

After the Dockyard modernisation from 1958, the number of berths was
reduced from three to two but there was no corresponding ease of congestion in the yard, as any gain in space was cancelled out by the two new
craneways and the prefabrication area. With the subsequent Scotts'
merger and later amalgamation with Lithgow in 1970, Cartsdyke substantially increased the tonnage of vessels built. In 1974 one of the 'daggers', which set the launching carriage in motion, failed with the 25,000
ton deadweight *British Tweed*. She slewed off the launching ways,
lurched down the slip damaging the ways and bounced off the frames of
the bulk carrier *Sugar Carrier* under construction in the adjacent berth.
The *British Tweed* was immediately drydocked after the launch but on
inspection revealed surprisingly little damage and, apart from a few shell
plates being scored and bent, she was found to be quite watertight. Sir
Eric Drake, Managing Director of owners, the B.P. Tanker Company,
joked about the mishap, at the post-launch lunch, and said that the accident was due to a failure to smear the ways with B.P. grease. The cause of
this unorthodox launch was never clearly established, although some time
after it was discovered that the concrete towards the end of the slip was

breaking up. An earlier launch, at the same berth, of the *Geeststar*, had been carried out with the water level only a little over the safe minimum and the ship possibly put too much pressure on the ways causing the piling to crumble.

At Scotts' in the early 1950s an Elder Dempster cargo liner was all 'set up' for her launch and craft had already taken up position in the Channel, with red flags hoisted to alert any shipping in the vicinity. However, a foreign-flagged ship, sailing upriver, slipped past the cordon seemingly quite oblivious to the situation. As the cargo liner began her slide, a tug went to head off the encroaching vessel and cut sharply across her bows with a great flourish. But this hasty manoeuvre was in vain and almost resulted in the tug capsizing. Only by chance was a collision averted as the foreigner realised the danger and went 'Full Astern' with both anchors down, the standard procedure in such an emergency. A similar incident, which involved a collision and fatalities, took place in 1941 on the Upper Reaches, amid a dense fog.

When the tanker *Scottish Hawk* was launched in 1955 by the Dockyard, the 'drag' anchor was dropped in the wrong spot. The launch took place amid a severe squall and the ship first struck the Garvel Beacon before careering across the Channel on to the Greenock Bank and grounding. When the *Swan River* was launched at the same yard in 1958, she sailed across the Channel before coming to rest just before the sandbank.

It was the practice following a launch for workers to rush down to the water's edge where they were frequently caught by a backwash wall of water which engulfed or drenched them. Large numbers of the labour force were always present at a launch as spectators, and in 1957 at the launch of the cargo ship *Lord Codrington* at Scotts' a joiner slipped on a greasy plank and fell on to an angle iron which was lying on the ground. At the same launch a forty-eight-year-old fitter collapsed as he was standing with his workmates. Both casualties were taken to hospital and detained.

The pieces of wood and shores from the launch were picked up afterwards and were usually to be found lying on the berth, by the waterfront or floating in the shallows. On one occasion at Scotts', 'Shores' McLeod, who was generally responsible for the shores, was doing some post-launch beachcombing. Wearing waders, he was searching in water several feet deep, when a ship steaming downriver caused a wash. 'Shores' had his back to the wave and, being distracted, failed to take evasive action, was knocked off his feet and left floundering.

A former office-girl at the Dockyard in the 1950s recalled the occasions immediately after launches when Mr. Swan brought in the tartan, retrieved from the smashed launch-bottle, to the office. The girls then had the task of extracting the tiny particles of glass and cutting the cloth into ribbons which were later presented as favours to the ladies invited to the post-launch lunch. If a Clan liner was being launched, the Chieftain of the appropriate Clan was also invited to attend.

Some launches did not take place on the scheduled date owing to long-term problems such as a strike but more immediate delays were often caused by adverse weather conditions. The *Swan River* was due to go into the water at 12.30 p.m. on the 1st December 1958 but thick fog had descended over the River for some days before and it was decided to go ahead with the launch only if visibility improved by some 300 yards. Irrespective of conditions, the naming ceremony would be performed and the official luncheon held. On the 1st the launch was postponed for thirty minutes in the unlikely event of an improvement in the weather. This failed to materialise and so, for the first time in twenty-five years, poor weather had prevented a launch at the Dockyard. While under construction the ship was referred to popularly as the *'Swanee' River* and the Managing Director made mention of this unofficial name in his speech at the launch. The weather cleared the following day and the launch took place in perfect conditions.

There was an amusing conclusion to the building of the *Swan River*. As she was built to carry grain, her owners insisted, prior to leaving the James Watt Dock on her delivery voyage to Swansea, that the holds be hosed down. She left Greenock in immaculate condition but to the astonishment and anguish of the Dockyard staff who accompanied her to South Wales, the first cargo loaded was in fact coal and tin plate; there was coal dust everywhere.

Bad weather conditions affected the launch of the Royal Navy submarine *Cachalot* at Scotts' on 10th December 1957. A distinguished gathering of over 100 had assembled on the platform as the weather deteriorated steadily towards the actual launching time. The ship was named amidst swirling snowflakes which made the River barely visible and, when a blinding snowstorm further reduced visibility to less than 100 yards, the launch was postponed. The lady who was to launch the warship later said what a great honour and privilege it had been to receive an invitation to launch a ship, few got that opportunity; and yet when her turn came she was to be denied that pleasure. It was also the occasion when the Chairman, Mr. A. Sinclair Scott, announced the major reorganisation scheme for Scotts' which was to make possible the construction of 40,000 ton deadweight tankers of up to 700 feet long. The berths were to be realigned

The launch of the Swan River *from Greenock Dockyard, December 1958. The launch was postponed the previous day owing to fog.*

and the new berths serviced by two large travelling cranes. There would be considerable extension of welding facilities with roads and railways also being repositioned. The *Cachalot* was launched the following day and in satisfactory weather conditions.

Incidentally the launch of the *Walrus*, a 'Porpoise' class submarine and sister ship of the *Cachalot*, in 1959 was significant in that for the first time in Scotts' history the ceremony was performed by a member of the Royal Family – the Duchess of Gloucester. The arrangements for the launch included the erection of extensive platforms, on either side of the slipway, to provide seating accommodation for over 3,000 spectators who included workers and staff of the yard and invited guests.

High winds also caused the postponement of several launches, for example the Royal Fleet Auxiliary ship *Resource* in 1966 at Scotts'; the *World President* at Cartsdyke in 1969; the Drillship *Ben Ocean Lancer* at Cartsdyke in 1976.

A former employee of the now defunct Joy Manufacturing Co., located in the east end of the town, recalled travelling to work in the summer of 1963. From the top deck of the bus, one day, he glanced over to Scotts' yard and contemplated the almost empty building berths. It was a quietish spell for the yard but he did notice a tiny hull on one of the slipways. He was amazed at the size, which was much smaller than any of the previous ships he had seen building there. The hull was that of the *Raylight* which was launched in September for local owners Ross & Marshall who had operated a 'puffer' fleet for many years. While under construction the *Raylight* was jokingly referred to locally as 'The puffer' being built at Scotts'.

The 'puffer' which had emerged in the late nineteenth century could be described as a steam coaster capable of carrying about 100 tons of cargo and approximately sixty-six feet long. The early ships of the type had non-condensing engines with the exhaust turned in towards the funnel. The resulting sound caused these vessels to be called 'puffers' – and the name stuck.

But the *Raylight* was certainly not a 'puffer' in the traditional sense, being motor-driven, twice the size and with a length of almost 100 feet. She had evolved from the original design and, although the name 'puffer' was something of an anachronism, there was some justification for this description. She was a fourth generation 'puffer' and like her predecessors was able to sit on the bottom if required at low tide to load or discharge cargo. In later years the *Raylight* was seen sitting on the sand at Tiree Harbour unloading coal.

One of the smallest vessels launched at Scotts' – the 'puffer' Raylight, *1963.*

As the coaster with her red, white and black funnel went down the ways and slipped into the water, men working on the submarine *Opportune* on a nearby berth stopped to cheer. Although the *Raylight* was the smallest ship to be built by Scotts' for seventy-five years, these workers were as proud of her launch as anything grander.

Major shipyards did build 'puffers' occasionally; for example, McMillan and Denny of Dumbarton. Scotts' had last launched a Ross & Marshall 'puffer' on 3rd September 1888, exactly seventy-five years before the *Raylight* launch and indeed went on to build a slightly larger sister ship, the *Dawnlight 1*, for the same owners in 1965. At the launch it was pointed out by the yard Managing Director that building the *Raylight* had secured jobs in the yard by providing continuity of labour between the end of one order and the beginning of another; the *Raylight* would begin her maiden voyage in a fortnight. As she was towed to the fitting-out basin it was observed that the tug handling her was of similar size.

With the advent of larger vessels the James Watt Dock has presented serious problems for pilots and it was here that many ships, built at Cartsdyke, were taken for completion. The entrance is in an awkward dog-leg position to the main channel and considerable manoeuvring is necessary to line up a ship for an accurate approach. In recent years several large cargo ships have sustained significant damage before tying up at the sugar berth. Newly-launched ships from Cartsdyke were under the additional handicap of a high freeboard and no power of their own. Workers from the adjacent Garvel Dry Dock were often interested spectators as it was usually to their advantage if a new ship suffered even minor damage in the transit of the entrance to the James Watt Dock.

After the merger with Scotts' in 1966, Cartsdyke started to build larger vessels, some of which were too big for fitting-out in the James Watt Dock. They were accommodated comfortably in Scotts' Basin and, after the merger with Lithgow, some Cartsdyke vessels even went to the Kingston Basin, Port Glasgow. The Cartsdyke yard built two 19,000 ton deadweight bulk carriers for the World Wide Shipping Co. of London in the late 1960s. As the *World President* and *World Hong Kong* were both designed for trading to the Canadian Lakes, fenders had to be fitted, thus ensuring protection to the hull sides while negotiating the locks of the Welland Canal. A protracted demarcation dispute ruled out the use of Scotts' Basin for fitting-out and the James Watt Dock was the only option. However, it was calculated that, with fenders added to the beam, the ships' safe passage into the Dock would be impossible. Despite the vessels being in a 'light' condition at the time of launching, the after fender would still have been low enough to catch the Dock sides. It was therefore decided to fit the fenders in drydock later and without them the ships squeezed through the Dock entrance with barely two feet to spare on either side.

A tight squeeze as the Rothesay Castle *is manoeuvred into the James Watt Dock for fitting-out in 1959, with the assistance of tugs* Chieftain *and* Wrestler. *The stern at the front of the photograph is of the* Clarkspey *launched the previous day at Lithgow.*

Chapter 7

Fitting-out

There were many specialist workers involved in the hard task of fitting-out or outfitting. These included joiners, plumbers, coppersmiths, iron-mongers, engineers, 'Black Smiths' and riggers who were occupied with anything to do with wires, ropes and fitting derricks. The shipwright installed and tested almost everything which, on the outside, included winches, derricks, masts, life-boats, gangways, anchor cables, handrails, deck laying and, on the inside, cabins, accommodation ladders, insulation and fridge work. Before 1939 if the weather was wet, for example, work was rained off and the men received no pay. In postwar years there was seldom a stoppage on outdoor work for bad weather, although the men were not issued with rain-proof clothing, and before the 1960s at Scotts' there were no hot showers available. In mid-winter with northeasterly winds blowing it was hell on deck. Hands stuck to the cold steel in freezing conditions; painful hacks developed on the fingers and as a result of the combined cold and wet there was the added agony of striking cold hands with tools and only 'softies' ever wore gloves. Deck-laying was one of the more arduous and time-consuming tasks but one which provided much job satisfaction.

In the late nineteenth century and early twentieth century much of the wood used by local yards came from the 'timber ponds' which extended over the sand flats between Woodhall at the east end of Port Glasgow and Langbank. Sturdy wooden posts, some twelve feet in height, stretched over 200 yards into the River and formed the numerous enclosures which made the 'ponds'. The wood lay in these 'ponds' for seasoning and, when ready, was floated back down to the yards by 'rafters'. Various companies had ownership of the 'ponds' and the timber was not exclusively for shipyard use. There was an occasion, for example, in the 1880s when a gentleman travelled across from Cowal to purchase two substantial beams for a major church roof repair. The 'ponds' lapsed into disuse in the 1920s.

Older workers recalled fondly the quality of the two-and-a-half inch thick decks on the many 'China boats' built at Scotts' some forty years ago. The work was demanding but the completed deck looked grand; the hand rails were also of teak. These ships were delivered to the China Navigation Company for service on the China coast. Other former workers remembered the 'China boats' more for the special anti-pirate metal railings around the superstructure. The passenger vessels *Chunking* and *Changchow* delivered in 1950 and 1951 were probably the best-appointed vessels built at Greenock since World War II.

With accommodation for forty-two first and 214 third class passengers they could also carry a good load of cargo. Close on 10,000 gross tons, they were the largest in a long line of vessels built at Scotts' for China Navigation and also the last. By the time the '*King* and '*Chow* were completed, the trade down the China coast and through the islands to Australia had dwindled to an uneconomic level. The *Chungking* was sold to the Admiralty after a few months trading and renamed *Retainer* but the *Changchow* was not even allowed to head for the China coast and was taken over by Scotts' and later fitted, as the *Resurgent*, for naval auxiliary work.

In the same period Scotts' built three vessels for the 'Blue Funnel' Line, which was more accurately known as the Alfred Holt Line. These ships had decks built of the cheaper Oregon pine and were contemptuously referred to by the workforce as belonging to the 'Hulk Line'. The 'Blue Flues' had a considerable area of wood decking – necessary for accommodating pilgrims, when voyaging in Far Eastern waters.

Deck laying was then followed by the process of 'caulking' which was necessary to stop up the seams between the planks. Until the early 1950s oakum was used for this purpose. The pleasant-smelling, untwisted tarry rope arrived in bales, had to be teased out, rolled into sticks and packed into the spaces. Four strands were needed, with the first one hammered home making a satisfying 'ping' sound; the third and fourth were much more difficult. In more recent years this became a power-assisted operation, with the oakum replaced by cotton which was much quicker to use and cleaner.

A former caulker at Cartsburn recalled an unusual incident while working with his squad which was involved in piece-work at the time. One member, who was intensely disliked by the others owing to his bullying and violent temper, had apparently covered a tremendous area of outer deck at a prodigious rate and in one shift. However, the secret of his success was soon revealed after a routine test was carried out. Red lead was poured over the oakum to check that the seams were watertight and it dripped through the caulker's work to the deck below. He was immediately sacked for his hasty and neglectful job.

Bad weather caused problems too and often in freezing temperatures the seams iced-up and a sawdust mix had to be inserted to melt the ice.

On one occasion a life-boat, being tested at Scotts', was filled with pig-iron ballast equal to the weight of a full complement of persons and lowered at an angle of 15-20 degrees. The Board of Trade inspectors, who were there, obviously expected the life-boat to reach the water at the contracted speed but it failed to meet the required standards and a time-consuming exercise followed. Unfortunately the life-boat could not be hauled back up via the davits with such a quantity of ballast; all the iron had to be unloaded and brought up to boat-deck level before the procedure could be repeated after all the necessary corrections had been made.

Younger workers had great problems trying to fit life-boat chocks on the *Fort Grange*, the first of the two sister ships built at Cartsburn for the Royal Fleet Auxiliary. The difficulty arose on account of naval vessels being built to different specifications than merchant ships. The boat assembly was of a much more traditional design than that of the contemporary merchant vessels to which the less experienced men were accustomed.

Even when a ship was safely berthed, after her launch from the Dockyard, under the big crane in the James Watt Dock, there was no guarantee that fitting-out would proceed without interruption. Dock traffic had priority and if, for example, an Elders Fyffes banana ship required the use of Shed E at the quayside adjacent to the fitting-out berth, a new ship might have to move further up the dock. Fortunately this was a fairly simple manoeuvre and the ship could be shifted by using hand-power with about twenty men operating a pulley-block system. There were complications when the sugar berth was also occupied and tugs were then required to move the new vessel across to the coaling berth.

The big crane in the James Watt Dock was built during World War I and completed in 1917. It was erected by Sir William Arrol & Co. for Greenock Harbour Trust who wanted to up-grade facilities for shipowners and shipbuilders. The 150-ton electric cantilever crane was built at a cost of £22,000. The crane was capable of revolving through 360° in either direction and was designed to deal with loads from 80 tons to 150 tons. The jib had a total length of 230 feet and was formed of two latticed box girders. The range of lift enabled the main hook to drop 30 feet below quay level and to rise 150 feet above it.

The official opening took place on the 30th May 1917, when the crane was set in motion with a weight of 200 tons being lifted and carried round, the revolution being completed in five minutes. A silver salver was presented to the Provost of Greenock by Arrol's and the inscription read, 'Presented to Provost William Bentley McMillan by Sir William Arrol & Co., Ltd. on the occasion of taking over by Greenock Trust of a 150-ton fitting-out crane, erected by Sir William Arrol & Co. Ltd. at James Watt Dock, Greenock, May 1917.'

Once, in the early 1960s the crane broke down. For some time and without anyone anticipating damage, the jib had been operating within a restricted radius which had put excessive strain on ball bearings in the main engine.

The cantilever crane was assisted by two steam cranes whose boilers had to be stoked up at 6.00 a.m. in order to get adequate steam-up for starting work at 7.45 a.m. These small cranes were very useful for lifting pipes, fittings and joinery materials on to the deck of a new ship. None of the three cranes were owned by the Cartsdyke yard, belonging initially to the Greenock Harbour Trust, then the Clyde Navigation Trust and finally the Clyde Port Authority. Ships having engines installed by the big crane were subjected to a time limit of ten days if another ship was waiting.

There were numerous cases of ships breaking their moorings while fitting-out in the James Watt Dock; this was caused by a severe wind build-up which funnelled down Ratho Street like a tornado and emerged directly on to the berth. One night in the winter of 1957, the new Clan liner *Ayrshire* broke loose, was swept across the dock by a gale-force wind and ended up wedged diagonally between the north and south quays, blocking the entrance to the Dock. When the mooring ropes snapped there was nobody on the ship and the Fire Brigade had to provide a forty-foot ladder to enable workmen to get on board to fix new ropes. The incident took place late on a Saturday night and a lorry toured the local pubs for some time before collecting a suitable squad of men. Hawsers were lowered to the quay and the *Ayrshire* was temporarily secured in position with her bows against the north wall and her stern overhanging the quay on the other side. The ship was later shifted back to her fitting-out berth on the afternoon tide but without the pilot. With tugs in position and ropes cast-off, he had been about to board the vessel when suddenly the stern swung out and the ship began to drift up the dock. The pilot was left bemused and stranded on the quayside with the re-berthing being carried on without him.

The *Ayrshire* suffered hull damage at the stern where rivets had popped out and some plates fractured. But her misfortune continued as a few weeks later a fifty-four-year-old shipyard labourer suffered severe head injuries and shortly after died in hospital after falling eighteen feet through an opening in the accommodation deck.

The *Clan Macgowan* was also a victim of severe winds in 1962 and in her case twenty-nine ropes snapped before she was driven across the dock and smashed into dockside equipment before coming to rest. She was reberthed the next day and eventually fitted with twelve new wires – six at the stern and six at the bow, each with nylon tails which added extra security for the ship at the quay.

In September 1958 the *Clan Maciver* almost capsized at the final stages of fitting-out; ballast trials had just taken place in the dock and the ship was shortly due to be dry-docked prior to commencement of sea trials. In the early hours of the morning of 25th September she started to list heavily and a hole, cut in the port side to facilitate the pumping out of the bilges, was brought under water level. When this happened water began to fill the engine room and the list rapidly increased until there was a grave danger of the ship 'turning turtle'. Both police and fire brigade were called out but could do little to stop the list. The ship strained her mooring hawsers to such a tension that they became white-hot and then snapped one after the other, amid a shower of sparks. At 4.00 a.m., after a gangway leading to the ship's deck from the quayside fell with a great crash just missing the firemen, the three employees who were on duty on board the *Clan Maciver* at the time were advised to jump ashore. A coaster, the *Devon Coast*, which had been moored alongside the Clan liner, was in extreme danger of being crushed and the crew was alerted just in time to effect her escape. Capsize was only averted when the sluice in the dock was opened and enough water let out to ensure that the ship rested on her port bilge on the bottom of the dock. Despite this measure she lay at an angle of some 35° and was still not completely out of danger.

Former office staff remembered the panic in the yard complex as they arrived for work later that morning and their own disbelief at what had happened.

A salvage team, from the Faslane shipbreaking company, Metal Industries, assisted by Admiralty divers and frogmen from the Boom Defence Depot at Greenock and the Gareloch, worked all night to restore the ship

The Clan Maciver listing at 35° in the James Watt Dock, September 1958.

The Clan Maciver listing at 35° in the James Watt Dock, September 1958.

The Geeststar *fitting out in the James Watt Dock, 1972.*

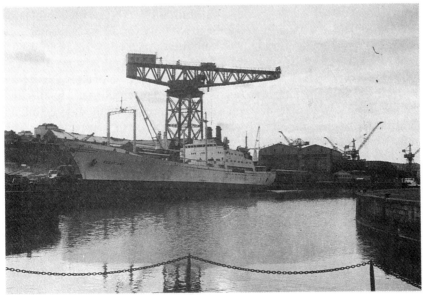

The Geestland *fitting out in the James Watt Dock, 1971.*

to an even keel. After locating and plugging the five-inch hole in the port side they were able to correct the list gradually.

Incredibly the *Clan Maciver* was not seriously damaged and her handing over to the Clan Line was only delayed by two weeks. A cartoon of the sinking, in the local paper, depicted the sunken *Clan Maciver* coming out in sympathy with the failure of the twelve-metre yacht *Sceptre*, the British challenger, to win the America's Cup. The *Clan Maciver* later became known in the Clan Line fleet as the *Clan Nautilus*.

There had been a previous instance of a new ship capsizing in the James Watt Dock, in October 1904, when the 3,000-ton full-rigged Belgian training ship *Comte de Smetde de Naeyer* suddenly keeled over and her masts crashed on to the quay, just missing a crowd of workmen. She had just been launched from the yard of the Greenock & Grangemouth Dockyard Co.

Awards of £3,000 were made by a jury in the Court of Session to the widow and son of a ship rigger who died as a result of an accident on board a ship fitting-out in the James Watt Dock in 1953. While crossing a hatch he fell into a hold because the hatch covers were unsupported and gave way beneath him. The Dockyard denied liability but was blamed for failing to secure the hatch covers.

A former shipwright talked about the great experience of working on one of the last ships to be built at Cartsburn, the Royal Fleet Auxiliary supply vessel *Fort Austin* which was finished to a very high standard. Naval work had always been rewarding, not only for the workers but also for the shipyard, as the 'gravy train' providing the major source of profit. He was reminded of the time when fitting-out was well advanced; it was the end of a day's work and, as foreman shipwright, he had responsibility for seeing that everything was left in a shipshape condition. He checked that the life-boats were lashed and accommodation ladders secured but on his tour discovered the ensign staff, above the stern, was missing. The studs which had bolted the sixteen-foot-long pole to a plate on the after deck had loosened and the pole was found dipping over the side with the tip some feet above water level. It was a stormy, murky night as the shipwright went out in a small boat in an attempt to retrieve the staff.

An ex-welder who worked at Cartsburn in the 1970s recalled the work done by industrial cleaners, Cameron's who moved in at the end of the day and cleaned all ships in the yard, at all stages of construction. Cameron's, who were known as the 'Cameroons', had free access to the yards at any time and often worked during the night, beginning at 8.00 p.m. and continuing until 6.00 a.m. They had the dirtiest of jobs, cleaning out tank bottoms, double bottoms and the bilges.

Chapter 8

Trials

I began to take a serious interest in ships in 1959 and at that time only had a very limited knowledge of the subject. It was summer, school holiday time, as I gazed with binoculars across the Holy Loch from the porch of 'Dunedin' by the shore road at Sandbank, and just along from the pier.

The loch was dotted with laid-up shipping; I saw several similar vessels, with funnels aft, moored in pairs, towards the Sandbank shore, all with the prefix *Empire* before their names. Further over towards Strone lay the tramp steamers *Ingleby* and *Bellerby*, with green hulls and chequered funnel motif. These inactive ships were chained to large buoys and obviously were going to be there for a prolonged period of lay-up, all with canvas cowls drawn over the funnel top. It was much later and only after much research that I was somewhat smugly able to find out about the 'Empire, Landing Ship Tanks' and that the *Ingleby* and *Bellerby* were originally wartime standard design-built ships latterly owned by Ropner.

My ship-spotting activities soon extended beyond the confines of the Holy Loch and from the Sandbank war memorial a great panorama, encompassing the entrance to the Holy Loch, Kilcreggan, the Tail o' the Bank, Gourock and the Cloch Lighthouse, opened up. For me it was always an exhilarating moment to round 'The Point' and see that view suddenly materialise.

The Clyde shipyards were doing great business then and enjoyed a boom which was to continue well into the 1960s but such was my ignorance that I often mistook a ship on trials for a trading vessel; and then it would slowly dawn on me that the ship which disappeared in the morning and reappeared off Hunter's Quay in the late afternoon was in fact brand new.

I never understood, then, why new ships spent so long idling at anchor off Loch Long or lazily manoeuvring in great circles. This lasted for a day or so before they started off down-Firth. But, of course, the ship was engaged in the early complexities of trials which ranged from anchor and windlass checks to compass adjustment and the testing of steering gear. It was only when these had been carried out effectively that the ship then proceeded with runs over the measured mile.

In common with shipping lines which used the Clyde regularly, Clyde shipyards employed 'Special pilots' to handle their ships. In addition the yards enabled the Clyde pilot to 'Take out Articles' and act as ship's Master during the trial period. This added considerable responsibilities to the pilot's remit but meant that trials could be carried out beyond Cumbrae Heads, where there was a much greater area of water to test the new ship. This provided the opportunity for eight-hour endurance trials and lengthy periods of prolonged steaming at full speed.

But the Dockyard did not approve of this flexible arrangement and their 'Special pilot' had to operate within the confines of the Upper Firth to conform with Clyde Pilotage regulations. A former Dockyard pilot revealed that his longest straight run was from the mouth of Loch Long to Kilchattan Bay, off Bute, and only lasted for approximately twenty-two minutes. There were further restrictions in that the pilot had to plan the 180° turn at the end of the run, some two miles in advance. Precise speed tests were carried out over the Skelmorlie Measured Mile, whilst many Glasgow yards used the Arran Mile.

Sometimes the rules had to be broken. In 1962, when the *Clan Graham* was on trials, weather conditions deteriorated to the extent that the pilot was unable to berth the ship at Princes Pier, Greenock, or even anchor overnight at the Tail o' the Bank. The cargo liner had to steam throughout the night and for safety reasons, outside Cumbrae Heads.

This incident caused much controversy over the insurance situation and with the Clan Line shipping master and other invited guests who had to spend an unscheduled night at sea.

At the end of successful trials, elements of informality were occasionally introduced. Mrs. Marples, wife of the then Transport Minister, launched the *Clan Macgowan* in 1962 and at the time indicated that she had never been in the Clyde area before. Some days after the ship's trials were over, Mrs. Marples was invited on board the vessel and a day was spent cruising round the Firth of Clyde; this included the bonus of a passage through the Largs Channel, between Largs and Cumbrae. When a ship was completed in 1960 and prior to her delivery voyage, Clan Line guests were fortunate to voyage on a mini-cruise as far as Stornoway in the Outer Hebrides; the pilot of the new *Rothesay Castle* in 1960 took her on a wide sweep of Rothesay Bay as a courtesy visit. Incidentally the Dockyard workers dubbed the *Rothesay Castle* and her sister ship *Rotherwick Castle* the 'Lavender Hill Mob', after the comedy film title and on account of their distinctive hull colour scheme.

While at the early trials stage in 1983 H.M.S. *Challenger* had a series of alarming confrontations with a Royal Fleet Auxiliary tanker in Scotts' Basin. The *Challenger*, a seabed operations vessel, was frequently in and about the dock and from time to time the small oiler had to come along-side and refuel or top up the naval ship. The first time the tanker came into the Basin, her speed was excessive, manoeuvring open to question and the bow smashed the *Challenger*'s accommodation ladder. The R.F.A.'s

The Clan Ross *on trials in 1965. She was the last ship to be completed by the Greenock Dockyard Co., Ltd. before that company was merged into the Scotts' group.*

navigation did not improve with practice and it was with great apprehension that the yard personnel, on board the *Challenger*, awaited each subsequent, menacing visit of the tanker.

Minor accidents were a common feature in the Basin. On one occasion a ship being pulled into the Dock was made fast at the stern, with rope and hawser, to a bollard. However, when the stern suddenly nudged out the rope went from slack to taut and a man on the quayside, whose feet were whipped from underneath him, was tossed in the air and landed in the water.

A ship was shortly due to leave the Basin on her delivery voyage; among supplies being loaded was a considerable consignment of beer and other alcoholic beverages which were carefully locked away in a secure store. Night-shift workers burnt a hole through the deck above and stole the liquor; with the assistance of a welder and caulker the breach was sealed and covered up.

A ship, repairing in the Scott Lithgow drydock, was taking on a supply of beer when a crate was accidentally dropped over the side as it was being carried down a companionway. Employees were later seen wading thigh deep in dirty water at the bottom of the dock, searching for unbroken bottles.

The last merchant ships to be constructed at Cartsdyke and Cartsburn were part of a three-ship order placed by Ocean Transport & Trading Ltd. for their Elder Dempster subsidiary. The design of these three 'M' class ships, built for the U.K. – West Africa liner route, was based on that of four earlier 'M' class vessels built in Japan. Owing to the company's 'Ocean' connection, the new ships were given traditional 'Blue Funnel' names – *Maron, Mentor* and *Myrmidon*. During the trials of the *Maron* it was found that vibration and noise were excessive and modifications were carried out reducing these to within acceptable limits.

The *Myrmidon*, a Cartsburn product, ran her trials in the autumn of 1980. A former worker remembered the unsatisfactory hatch design; they fitted badly, were not watertight and at the first 'Emergency hatch opening' trial numerous problems resulted. In general the shipwright enjoyed trials, describing the period as being similar to a paid holiday. However, total relaxation was not possible as constant 'On Call' duty meant many a broken night's sleep. For him, the trials of the *Myrmidon* were memorable, not on account of faulty hatches but for an embarrassing incident when the Department of Trade representative requested an anchor test. The anchor squad released the cable but, unfortunately, as the chain rattled out the anchor became detached. The 'LOST ANCHOR' signal

The last merchant ship to be built at Cartsburn; the Myrmidon *on trials, 1980.*

The last ship to be built at Cartsburn, H.M.S. Challenger, *on the upper Reaches of the Clyde, 1986.*

was flashed as around £14,000 worth of anchor lay on the seabed; later attempts to locate and salvage it were unsuccessful. A later revelation was that the anchor gear had been fitted in the Scott Lithgow drydock by a squad of shipwrights who were relatively inexperienced in this type of work. One of the links was weakened owing to a badly fitted pin which had simply slipped out during the trial.

During trials the *Banbury*, built at Cartsburn in 1972, had occasion to anchor at the Tail o' the Bank when the tanker *Kong Haakon VII* almost severed her anchor cable.

When the *Challenger* was on trials she had on board a significant naval complement in addition to the shipyard workers, who had problems trying to interpret the naval vernacular, especially any communications directed from the officers. One day as she was steaming off Largs, going 'AHEAD', at a modest seven knots, the anchor squad received the message, issued from the bridge, that the starboard anchor be dropped. The foreman of the squad considered the likely result of letting the anchor go in such circumstances but gave way to his better judgement and decided that the order must be carried out. The anchor was released; the ship stopped dead and birled round violently with the pilot believing that the ship was going to sink. As the cable paid out the noise, dust and stour added to the mayhem before the brake was put on. Obviously a command had become muddled and scrambled *en route* from bridge to bow.

The *Challenger* was serviced by Clyde Marine Motoring's *Rover* or *Second Snark*, which could arrive at any time to take the shipyard workers ashore. Many a meal was hastily abandoned as the cry 'Last call for the *Second Snark*' reverberated round the *Challenger* at her Tail o' the Bank anchorage.

It was realised belatedly that no official colour photograph had been taken of the bulk carrier *World President* on sea trials in 1969. A director of Scotts' rushed down to the Greenock Esplanade and fortunately was able to capture the ship with a zoom lens on his camera as she was leaving the Clyde on her delivery voyage.

Chapter 9

Tour of the derelict yards

Until fairly recently I knew very little about the local yards. I often made my own way to Sandbank, sometimes from Glasgow to Dunoon by steamer which provided a reasonable view of shipbuilding from the River; more often travel was from Glasgow by train, which offered a brief and somewhat obstructed view, from behind Scotts' engine works, between Cartsdyke and Greenock Central railway stations. With face pressed against the carriage window I squinted for a name on the bow of a ship nearing launching at Cartsburn and, feeling self-conscious, tried to conceal my excitement and anxiety from the other passengers. They would not have understood such behaviour unless, of course, they had a similar passion for ships. The biggest disappointment was to see an almost completed hull on the stocks but, tantalisingly, one without a name.

Even when living and working in the Inverclyde area from 1971, I never at any time before 1987 attempted to venture into the yards; maybe it was the intimidation of the imposing boundary wall and buildings, or perhaps an intrusion would have shattered the air of mystery which I had imagined within the Greenock yards. Content to leave the interior alone, glimpses from the outside gave me enough of a thrill; sometimes the main gate at Scotts' was open and I caught sight of a submarine, inside the Cartsburn drydock, with the conning tower shrouded with a green tarpaulin and webbed with scaffolding.

On Sunday afternoons in the early 1970s I often used to trudge alongside the rear perimeter of the yards *en route* to view shipping in the James Watt Dock and, on passing Cartsdyke, might see the high, bluff bows of a bulk carrier or tanker looming over the wall beside the entrance; the lifeboats perched on the flat roof of the foreman's building, awaiting the final shift to an adjacent superstructure.

I remembered too the notorious traffic hold-ups as the yards 'came out' at 4.30 p.m., when the tide of men flooded out of the main gates, surged across the road and sought out the homeward-bound buses.

In March 1987 the Scottish Development Agency bought forty-five acres of former shipyard and engineering land from Trafalgar House for redevelopment as an industrial or business park. The site had been previously owned by Scott Lithgow and included in the sale were the Cartsburn and Cartsdyke yards and Scotts' former engine works.

I wanted to visit the yards before demolition commenced, to savour some of the atmosphere but above all to see what they looked like, ironically for the first time. The necessary arrangement was made without any great difficulty and it was with great anticipation that I stood outside the gate at Cartsburn one July morning in 1987, awaiting the arrival of my guide from the 'Inverclyde Initiative' senior management team. Perversely, I realised my motivation to visit the derelict yards was greater than any urge I had had to visit them in their heyday.

After we had been through the formalities of security clearance, I was driven through one of the cavernous sheds at the rear of Cartsburn. This shed had been used for light-plate assembly but was now quite empty, as much of the plant and other machinery had already been disposed of. We sped along and I was informed that the immediate plan would involve the total demolition of all structures and buildings within the yards. When I somewhat optimistically inquired about the possibility of the preservation of just one crane for posterity, it was quickly affirmed that all structures would come down, although the dry dock, which could be traced back to 1810, would remain owing to its historic value. Crane demolition would be relatively straightforward and present no great problem; the main difficulty would be the uprooting of the slips' great concrete foundations. After basic demolition and site clearance, land engineering would be carried out to remove floor slabs and general foundations; levelling would then be undertaken.

I was dropped off at the east end of Cartsburn and left free to meander on my own. There was momentary gloom when passing through the empty vastness of a former welding shed before emerging into sunlight and the Cartsdyke sector. Cartsdyke had always appealed to me, although a reason could not be pinpointed. Perhaps because it had been known affectionately as the 'wee yerd'.

An assortment of redundant shipyard equipment, much of it hidden by shrubbery, littered the site. However, the two concrete slipways, which stretched 600 feet in length and declined slightly towards the water's

The last launch at Cartsdyke, the Mentor, *August 1979.*

edge, were relatively clear of vegetation. I glanced over to the west slip where the cargo liner *Mentor* was launched on 9th August 1979; she signalled the end of an era, being the last launch from Cartsdyke.

A few logs similar in size and appearance to telegraph poles lay amidst the small copse at the head of the berths. The larger ones had no doubt been used as side-shores to prop up the sides of the ship's uncompleted hull and the smaller, squatter ones used as bilge shores supporting the bottom of the hull. In the same location were also great blocks of timber, strewn about in a very haphazard fashion; the rectangular chunks probably had made up part of the 'standing' or 'fixed ways' upon which a ship slid down at her launch; the wedge-shaped pieces had been part of the 'sliding ways'. I noticed a discarded protective face-mask used by a welder, a large rusty spanner and numerous concrete keel blocks of varied size. I mused over the blocks and wondered how many bottoms they had supported.

For me the outstanding feature of the derelict yard was lying high and dry alongside some of the timbers. The large dingy, with the wording

Abandoned wooden shores and concrete keel blocks, Cartsdyke, 1987.

CARTSDYKE CAPS DEPT. on the stern, was not in bad shape, with most of her planking intact, although the bow had sprung slightly. There was a small, metal plate screwed on to the inside of the transom with a yard name and number indicating her origin from an English boatyard on the east coast. The picking-up of floating wood after a launch would have been one of her tasks; another, to retrieve isolated shores dislodged from the stern of a ship on the stocks, by a high tide or storm. What a marvellous feeling it was to come across such an interesting and surprising object.

The yard was still dominated by the four travelling cranes built by Butters Bros. as part of the Cartsdyke modernisation in 1957. I looked up at these pyramid-shaped machines, which were all still intact with hooks dangling idly at the end of the skyward-pointing jibs. They were in poor condition and all the cabs had several broken windows; rust showed through the faded light-blue paintwork. One had been effectively immobilised in 1984 when thieves damaged much of the electrical installation.

The Cartsdyke dinghy amidst launch timbers, 1987.

A derelict crane on the east ramp at Cartsdyke, 1987.

It was a huge, enclosed space and I found it difficult to imagine how restricted it had been when two hulls were building simultaneously, and how claustrophobic for the labour force. I spent over an hour in the compact Cartsdyke yard before moving back through to the east end of Cartsburn.

To my left was an extensive assortment of shedding and, on the right, the berths and cranes. What an enormous area sprawled out before me and the openness was exaggerated by the empty berths. Vegetation was more limited here, with only the odd bush thickly flourishing beside the largest slipways. There was a distinct air of dilapidation about the whole site; an eerie stillness pervaded and there was no sound except for the seagulls, which I had probably disturbed, screeching and wheeling high above. I was alone in the yard and the atmosphere was reminiscent of 'Willie Rough's' comment of 'Deserted shipyards . . . like a grave yaird full o' bogie men.' Two lofty, fixed tower cranes stood directly to my right and between them and extending over the former submarine slip was an orderly stack of 'shores' and keel blocks. This pair of cranes could so easily have been 'Rough's' 'Big cranns looking down like vultures'. Contemplating the nearest of the two, I noticed a large plate bolted to the lower cross frames. This identified the maker as Sir William Arrol & Co., Ltd. of Glasgow who had built the crane as job number 4682 in 1945. The manufacturer had also recommended that 'the load was not to exceed 20 tons at 100 feet radius and 15 tons at 130 feet radius.'

It was on the naval berth that a ten-year association with Australia and the Lower Clyde ended with the launch of the Australian submarine *Otama* by Princess Anne in December 1975. This was the first submarine

The seaward twenty-ton crane with its jib pointing over the former submarine berth at Cartsburn, 1987.

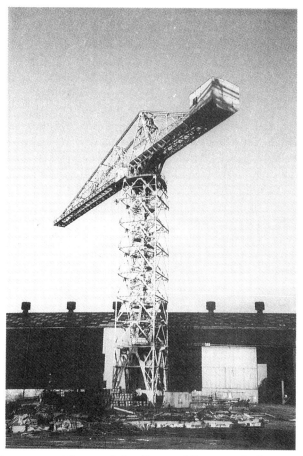

The twenty-ton crane, at the top of the slip, presiding over the former submarine berth at Cartsburn, 1987.

launched by the Princess and the last of the six 'Oberon' class submarines built for Australia in Greenock. The *Otama*, launched on the same day as her sister ship *Onslow* by Princess Alexandra in 1968, slipped into the Clyde to the strains of 'Waltzing Matilda.' The *Otama* was also the last submarine to be built at Cartsburn.

Further across were the two largest and most modern of the Cartsburn cranes. The travelling cranes, which had been a key part of the massive development programme of the early 1960s, were built by Arrol in 1960, had a maximum load capacity of sixty tons, straddled a huge ramp and

The launch of the last submarine built at Cartsburn, the Otama, *1975.*

The last merchant ship launch at Cartsburn, the Myrmidon, 1980.

serviced berths on either side. Curiously, I did not find them quite so impressive as the twenty tonners.

The last launch of a merchant ship at Cartsburn took place on the berth immediately to the west of these cranes, in February 1980. The *Myrmidon* was the last of the trio ordered from Scott Lithgow by the Ocean Transport and Trading Ltd. Prior to the launch, Mr. A. Ross Belch, Chairman of Scott Lithgow, had referred to the generally unhealthy state of shipbuilding at the time and pointed out that the launch would be the first and last launch on the Lower Clyde in 1980. The ship was launched, amid great cheers from a large number of yard workers and spectators, by Mrs. Peggy Ellerton, wife of a Director of the owning shipping company. Her husband, speaking at the post-launch luncheon, described the ship as 'the latest but not I hope the last of a long and famous line of ships built by Scotts' for our company.'

I weaved my way, with some difficulty, across the great concrete expanse of abandoned building berths. The site was really in an awful state and included a variety of discarded materials, such as solitary keel blocks, numerous wooden ladders of different dimensions, bits of timber, iron

The westward slip at Cartsburn from the sixty-ton crane ramp, 1987.

bars and masses of coiled wire. The security men had interrupted already intruders intent on a nighttime plunder. And it was from here that Cartsburn had launched its last ever ship, the sea bed operations vessel H.M.S. *Challenger* in 1981. A detail of that launch had stuck with me, as I recalled that the champagne blew backwards, soaking the launching party.

On the western side of the main slipway area was a pair of quaint twelve-ton cranes which had no maker's name plate attached. However, they were obviously much older than the ones I had already examined and sported a form of wind vane at the rear of the cab. This design feature would have helped the jib to pivot.

On the east side of the fitting-out Basin was another curio taking the form of a travelling crane. This one had a particularly distinctive shape and a close inspection led to me discovering an old, black telephone tucked away in a recess on a low section of the crane at about chest height – no doubt used for communicating instructions to the cab.

Wandering round the head of the fitting-out Basin I noticed the slight disturbance in the water where the Cartsburn stream flowed into the Clyde. There were two more second generation tower cranes of the twelve-ton design on the far side of the Basin and, in between them, the

The travelling crane beside the fitting-out Basin, Cartsburn, 1987.

two huge solid blocks of concrete which had formerly supported a 100-ton crane. The two twelve-tonners had been relocated from the berths at the time of modernisation.

I reflected that in the mid 1970s there were as many as six tower crane manufacturers in Britain. In 1987 there were none.

Crane drivers were usually designated to a particular crane; there was little mobility on their part, although occasionally they were required to operate one of the other 'cranns'.

One former craneman had spent most of his fourteen years in the yards in association with a sixty-ton mobile hammerhead at Cartsburn. His day shift began at 7.40 a.m., when he would ascend the ladders inside the crane's framework. There were no lifts and the ninety-five-foot climb to the cab was both time-consuming and energy-sapping.

His eyrie was tiny, cluttered and allowed for very limited movement; the motor room was six feet high, five feet wide and some three feet deep. However, conditions were exceptionally cosy; the driver sat on a deeply-cushioned chair, in his wee box, with handles, gears and brake levers within easy reach. Facilities included a kettle, a small cooker, transistor, V.H.F. radio, portable TV and even a 'library' of some thirty books. The equipment in the cab ensured a self-sufficiency which prevented the driver having to make an inconvenient descent during official break periods.

The literature was especially useful during 'slack' periods or in a hiatus when the crane was 'holding on to a job'. Also during quiet spells the operator often stretched his legs and walked to the end of the hammerhead catwalk. This also enabled him to carry out routine engineering maintenance.

The V.H.F. radio link with the ground kept up an efficient level of instruction and communication. But local residents who happened to tune into the same frequency were often appalled at the crude language used; complaints were common.

The operational skills of an experienced crane driver attracted considerable attention. It was possible for him to execute three or four actions simultaneously: lower the hook, slew the hammerhead right or left towards the job and move a mobile crane.

When new, the cranes all had clearly displayed guidelines as to recommended position of hook and corresponding load to be carried. These were printed in large lettering on boards positioned at various intervals along the hammerhead. But the boards, in time, soon fell off and the craneman had to rely on his own experience and intuition.

The sixty-tonners were excellent to operate, owing to their very powerful engines located with other machinery in the large wheelhouse at the
rear of the hammerhead. The hammerhead moved effortlessly into the
wind, unlike the sluggish and erratic hammerhead movements of the
older cranes carrying out a similar manoeuvre. Incidentally, when wind
speed reached a velocity of thirty-five m.p.h. work by all cranes was
suspended.

A former craneman who worked for a time on a twenty-ton hammerhead by the submarine berth, remembered lifting completed hull sections
on to the berth through a hole cut in the roof of the adjacent welding shed.
This practice, however, was soon discontinued on hazardous grounds. He
also recalled lifting 'uprights' into position around the outline drawing of
a ship due to be started on the berth.

Another ex-crane driver referred to the time when he was working with
the old twenty-five-ton travelling crane at the fitting-out basin. He was
lunching some distance away, having previously put the brake on the
wheels of the crane which was left 'holding on to a job' – in this case a
propeller shaft – at the head of the Basin. His break was rudely interrupted
when a somewhat breathless informer told him that the crane was trun-
dling, slowly, down the jetty towards the River. The operator gave chase
to the runaway crane, hauled himself on board, struggled into the cab and
pulled on the brake. When the crane finally came to a halt, large wooden
wedges were inserted under the front wheels. After this incident stringent
new rules were applied, indicating that cranes 'holding on to a job' should
not be left unattended.

In the 1970s the odd, temporary, telescopic-type crane similar to that
used on building sites appeared at Cartsburn. As the ship evolved on the
slipway, the 'wrecker' extended upwards. It was excellent for handling
small and light loads and took a maximum lift of about eight tons.

A version from France was erected at the fitting-out basin. One night a
hurricane-force wind lashed the crane, the jib of which crashed into the
Basin missing a Chilean submarine by only a few feet. The normal procedure at the end of the working day was to leave the jib or hammerhead
brake off to allow freedom of rotation in the event of windy conditions.
The brake, unfortunately, had been left on and the wind had put excessive
strain on the fixed jib, which had snapped off and fallen.

There were numerous other incidents involving the yard cranes over the
years. In the 1950s a strong wind felled a crane at Cartsburn, and in the
1960s the alloy jib of a swan-necked Cartsdyke crane collapsed and
toppled. Sometimes chances were taken by the crane driver and excessive

loads were dropped; mast-housing being lifted on to H.M.S. *Challenger* fell and crashed to the deck with damage in excess of £20,000.

Cranes, too, were involved in serious accidents. In the 1970s as a propeller shaft, on a sling, was being lowered to the ground, it slipped and the man waiting to receive the shaft was crushed to death by the weight of some 140 tons.

In the same period an engineer, who was fixing brakes on the wheels of a crane, lost all his toes. The driver, on hearing the cry 'Go Now!' had assumed the repair to be complete, put the crane into gear and the unsuspecting engineer was taken totally by surprise.

Many decisions were left up to the craneman and his judgement and opinion was always respected by the yard managers.

From the vantage point of the Basin, I noticed the isolated shacks dotted at random about the yard. A closer look showed inside walls covered in graffiti which included the autographed scrawls of former employees.

Before leaving the Cartsburn site, I visited the office building at the rear and, on my way there, passed one of the rockeries built to commemorate Scotts' 150th anniversary in 1961. I paused briefly at each floor but the spacious rooms were quite empty. However, in a cupboard near the top of the building was a great pile of publicity brochures advertising the trials of vessels built at Cartsdyke and Cartsburn in the 1970s. This idea had probably been initiated with the merger with Lithgow in 1970. Most of these had a glossy cover photograph and a comprehensive list of technical data, and the contents also included reference to such items as basic design specifications, hull sub-contractors and engine sub-contractors. It was only after flicking through one such pamphlet (See Appendix 1, p.113), describing details of the bulk carrier *Baknes*, built at Cartsdyke by Scotts' in 1970, that I appreciated the incredible quantity of components which went into the building of a ship. Hull sub-contractors alone supplied over fifty items of fitments and equipment which included anchor cables manufactured by W. L. Byers & Co., Ltd.; hospital beds by William Hume & Co., Ltd.; Velle Cranes by Cargo Speed Equipment Ltd. and window wipers by Wyn Struments Ltd. Machinery sub-contractors provided over seventy-five items, which included main engines by Burmeister & Wain (installed by J. G. Kincaid); propeller by Stone Maganese Marine; whistles by Industrial & Mining Supplies Co., Ltd.; sludge pump by G. & J. Weir. Most of the 100 or so sub-contractors were British and the extent of the list reflected clearly the general impact of a ship order – outwith the basic shipyard contribution.

My whistle-stop tour had taken over two and a half hours and it was with some poignant thoughts that I left the yards. I had been very much

Greenock, gashed with the scar of the derelict industrial site of Scotts' – shortly before site demolition began in 1987.

struck by the tremendous grandeur of Cartsburn and the sad emptiness of the vacant industrial complex. The strength of the past runs deep in peoples' feelings; they are reluctant to let go of the past and I wondered how those with a yard connection would react to the impending demolition and subsequent redevelopment.

Chapter 10

Demolition

The demolition contract was awarded to George Beattie & Sons of Kilsyth, in November 1987. There was not much activity on the waterfront site until the beginning of 1988 as Beatties' were initially preoccupied with Scotts' engine works.

I wanted to get a memento or artefact and, after waiting until work was underway, I ventured into the old shipyard in March 1988. The cranes were still intact as I carefully picked my way through Cartsburn but general demolition was going on apace; heavy plant machinery lumbered along noisily in all directions with the caterpillar tracks ploughing muddy furrows. I was *en route* to the Cartsdyke sector to negotiate with George Beattie Jnr., site foreman and a director of the firm, and I continued to follow an erratic path, dodging parapets of oozing mud and ponds of casual water; wellington boots would have been much more appropriate footwear than a pair of light shoes.

At Cartsdyke the four cranes had already been felled, were unrecognisable and lay crumpled and smashed on their sides. Mr. Beattie indicated that this operation had presented no problems as the cranes were simply pulled over.

It was quite fascinating to watch the relentless, mechanical, snarling movements of a huge excavator as the teeth of its bucket, at the end of a boom and jib, tore and clawed at the remaining brick-work of the Cartsdyke foreman's building. The driver was George Beattie's cousin who was still involved apparently in the learning process before he graduated to an even more powerful behemoth.

George found my request for a name plate somewhat unusual and puzzling but he would arrange it for a modest fee. I selected a plate from one of the 1945 twenty-tonners and about thirty minutes later two men,

A felled crane at Cartsdyke in 1988.

one with a burning torch, ascended the crane. A third man was hoisted up in an excavator's bucket, which was positioned below the name plate, and that man would catch hold of the plate as it became detached. The operation was not expected to take long with the plate believed to be of aluminium. However, it took over fifteen minutes to burn through the bolts and as I looked up the man in the bucket swore intermittently as the sparks rained down on his bare, upstretched arms and hands. With three bolts sheared off the plate swung slowly above the bucket the occupant of which then took the full strain as the final bolt was cut off. He buckled under the unexpected weight of cast-iron. At last, after a job lasting forty minutes overall, the plate, with some help, was manoeuvred safely into the grab which was brought to the ground. The plate was then lifted by four labourers into a truck, which George drove to the main gate where the car was parked.

George and I wrestled the heavy plate into the rear of the hatchback but, even with the seat down, one quarter of the plate protruded. At this point I just wanted to get away as quickly as possible and felt distinctly uncomfortable about the time and effort my request had involved. The suspension survived the very slow journey home and, although unloading pre-

The last crane left standing at Cartsburn shortly before its demolition.
The wind vane can be seen clearly and the large concrete block was
one of the foundations for the old 100-ton crane.

sented further problems, overcome only with a neighbour's help, I had
secured, triumphantly, a relic from the fast-disappearing shipyard.

After the March visit I went back only now and again to the site but
kept up with demolition progress which was comprehensively reported in
the local newspaper. One day in April a huddle of former workers stood
near the Cartsburn main gate, reminiscing about the war years, and an old
plater recalled proudly the building of H.M. cruiser *Bonaventure*; another
mentioned the innovation of the washing and shower facilities at Scotts'

A crane name-plate from Cartsburn.

in 1960, quite a novelty in a European shipyard at the time; a third man gazed over to Cartsdyke, which he described as 'slave labour camp' and concluded that demolition 'was the best thing for the place'.

After the Cartsdyke cranes were knocked down, the demolishers returned to Cartsburn and the east side of the fitting-out Basin where the travelling crane was cut down in April.

By the end of April the two twelve-tonners towards the west end of the Cartsburn slipway had gone. Much of the extensive shedding had also disappeared by this time, although the huge welding shed, at right angles to the water, had been reduced to a skeleton framework and was to be dismantled carefully before being reassembled for further use in London.

By mid-May the twenty-tonners were down and the second of the two sixty-ton travelling cranes was spectacularly grounded with the assistance of a controlled explosion in front of a large crowd of public and press on 1st June.

On 5th July, from the sixth level of the multi-storey car park in West Stewart Street, Greenock, I saw a solitary crane standing at the west end of the fitting-out basin and I wondered, absurdly, how it might have felt to

The twisted remains of the twenty-five ton travelling crane, April 1988. A sixty-tonner is standing to the right.

Looking beyond Scotts' graving dock to the last crane left standing.

be the last remaining crane; by 12th August there was no trace left of any crane.

The office block clock-tower, which was the last building of any substance to be floored, stood for a while in isolation like some medieval keep until it was brought down, at around midnight, on Saturday 8th July. The unusual timing was necessary to enable police to close off a section of the adjacent main road, for safety purposes, during a quiet spell.

The clock tower shortly before its demolition in July 1988.

Consequently, by the summer of 1988 not a building nor crane remained; the site had been neatly and efficiently cleared, although there were still several enormous mounds of rubble remaining but these were soon to be chewed up by a machine and ground into much finer material. This was to be used for infilling purposes connected with other Initiative projects. Some was to cover a new sewage pipe leading seawards from the Battery Park, Greenock. But the greatest revelation was the vast, open space providing an uninterrupted view of the Clyde from the road.

After the general clearance of the yard, slipways had to be torn up and the site levelled before any new construction could be carried out. Much of this work continued under other contractors throughout the winter and spring of 1988-1989. Pending this excavation, labourers uncovered old tools, boots and overalls from the water's edge. On one occasion a group of workers had gone for a lunch break to a pub across the road. Former shipyard men showed their resentment by assaulting the workers whom they believed had contributed directly to the termination of their former place of employment.

Even as the yards lay derelict, it had always been reassuring to see the cranes appear as you travelled westwards along the main thoroughfare

The cleared site Cartsburn/Cartsdyke looking northeast, July 1988.

from Port Glasgow. At first you saw the smaller cranes of Cartsdyke and then the larger, tower cranes of Cartsburn looming behind. By the end of June 1989 it was reported that a £7.6m development was to take place 'on

An aerial view of the cleared Cartsburn/Cartsdyke site, July 1988.

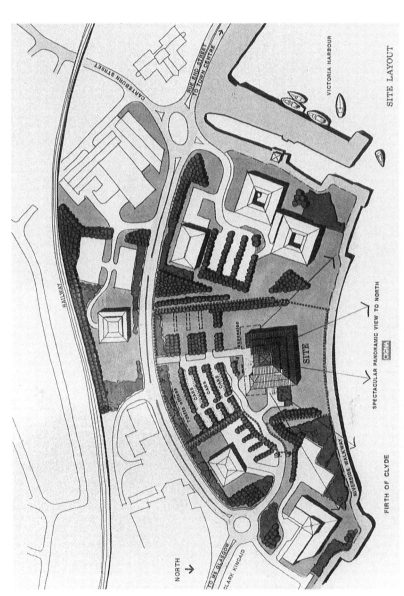

Crusader Insurance proposals for Cartsburn, 1989.

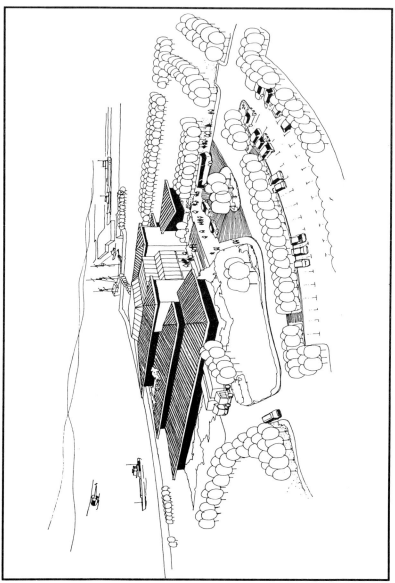

Crusader Insurance proposals for Cartsburn, 1989.

the site of the former Scotts' shipyard. The American insurance corporation 'Crusader' would centralise all their head office functions in a purpose-built 70,000 square foot office suite.'[1]

The James Watt Dock remained unaffected as the demolition of the yards progressed. The dark, hammerhead 'Titan Cantiliver' crane still dominated the quay where so many of the Greenock Dockyard ships were fitted-out. Only forty-two of this type of crane were built worldwide and apparently only fifteen remain, four of them on the Clyde. The Greenock model is now protected as a listed building and a larger counterpart at

The mobile crane, James Watt Dock, 1989. Latterly the crane was converted to diesel. It used to have a funnel when steam-driven.

[1] *Greenock Telegraph.*

Kvaerner Govan, formerly Govan Shipbuilders and before that Fairfield, has achieved similar status but is shortly to be demolished owing to proposed modernisation plans. Tucked away in a corner of the Dock's west end quayside lay the formerly industrious mobile steam crane which had often attended new ships. In 1989 it looked most forlorn and neglected.

Since the closure of Cartsdyke the only vessels to be fitted out in the Watt Dock have been built by Ferguson of Port Glasgow, a yard subjected to several title changes in recent years. As Appledore Ferguson they completed the *Lord of the Isles* for Caledonian MacBrayne in 1989.

However, the quay, a few years ago, was best known for a drugs-related incident. It was not uncommon for a ship, having discharged at the sugar berth further up the Dock, to lie waiting for orders beneath the crane. For some time, in the late Spring of 1988, the Panamanian cargo ship *San Vicente* was berthed there. She was fairly typical of the medium-sized vessel which brought in sugar to Greenock. Of about 5,000 tons gross, with engines aft, she had arrived from the West Indies on 15th April but the circumstances of her temporary lay-up were unusual. She was the

The Lord of the Isles *at the fitting-out berth, James Watt Dock, 1989.*

subject of a drugs investigation and International Intelligence reports to local customs had indicated the likelihood that the *San Vincente* was carrying a considerable quantity of cocaine.

Over 100 customs officials and police had the ship under surveillance for several days before taking action which resulted in twenty-two kilos of the drug being found in the ship's engine room. The cocaine was so well concealed that it took several days for a customs rummage crew to find the consignment. A further five kilos, which had already left the ship while she was unloading at Greenock, was traced to the former chief officer. The street value of the twenty-seven kilos was over £3 million and was the biggest quantity of cocaine ever recovered from a ship in Britain.

However, the situation was not unique to the James Watt Dock as in 1959 about thirty pounds of Indian hemp, worth more than £20,000, was seized by customs officials making a search of the cargo liner *Prome* while she was discharging 3,000 tons of cotton seed from Rangoon.

In 1990, apart from the Cartsburn graving dock, whose future was by no means assured, the big crane and the Garvel drydock, there was no

The San Vicente *beneath the big crane at the James Watt Dock, April 1988.*

The 4.15 to Cartsdyke

tangible legacy of major shipbuilding remaining in Greenock. But even the Garvel drydock has not been free of incident. In October 1977 a nine-year-old boy was rushed to the Southern General Hospital in Glasgow with a suspected fractured skull. He had been climbing down a rope, into the drydock, when the knot securing it to a railing slipped and he fell to the bottom of the dock.

The Durrington, Garvel Drydock, 1990.

And whenever I glance at the gloomy crane I am reminded, not just of its contribution to local shipbuilding, but of the sixteen-year-old worker who fell 153 feet to his death shortly before the crane was completed. While working on the jib he missed his footing, stepped into space and plunged to the ground.

The sturdy wooden posts, which formed the tight enclosures of the timber ponds between Woodhall and Langbank, have been eroded by weather and water and many are now grotesque, jagged, rotten stumps. But they are still a prominent landmark at low tide as they proudly maintain alignment and extend over the sand flats.

Some of the remaining posts of the timber ponds, July 1991.

The end of a day's work at Scotts', from 1961.

Appendix 1

M.V. "BAKNES"

FINAL TRIALS

On Firth of Clyde

Thursday, 5th February, 1970

M.V. Baknes.

SHIP No. 1175 — m.v. "BAKNES"

The bulk carrier "Baknes" has been built in Scotts' Shipbuilding Co. (1969) Ltd., Cartsdyke Yard for H. C. Clarkson & Co. Ltd., of London. The vessel as launched on 30th September, 1969, by Mrs L. A. Baker, wife of Mr L. A. Baker, a director of H. C. Clarkson & Co. Ltd.

The main machinery for the vessel has been manufactured by Burmeister & Wain, Copenhagen and installed by John G. Kincaid & Co. Ltd., Greenock.

The ship is the fourth of a series of eight bulk carriers ordered from Scott Lithgow by Jebsens and their associates. The vessel is of new design with full automation suitable for an unmanned engine room. She has been specially designed for the carriage of all types of grain, without shifting boards. Other bulk cargoes, such as cement, coal, iron ore, etc., can be carried in her spacious holds, also timber cargoes above and below decks.

The following are the principal particulars of the vessel:—

Length Overall	520 ft. 0 in.
Length B.P. on design draft of 30 ft. 0 in.	495 ft. 0 in.
Breadth Moulded	74 ft. 10½ in.
Depth Moulded to Upper Deck	42 ft. 0 in.
Loaded summer draft	31 ft. 3½ in.
Loaded timber draft...	31 ft. 9⅜ in.
Deadweight on summer draft	21,206 tons
Total water ballast	8,136 tons
Total grain capacity	919,348 cu.ft.
Designed trial speed (loaded)	about 14¾ knots

The "Baknes" has been built under special survey of Lloyds 1.A.1 strengthened for ore cargoes, holds Nos. 2 and 5 may be empty. The hold bulkheads are strengthened for the carriage of cement in bulk. She also meets the requirements of B.O.T. and complies with the Suez and Panama Canal Regulations. She is equipped for navigation of the St. Lawrence Seaway.

The vessel is of the single deck type with poop and forecastle, a raked stem with a ram bow and a transom stern. She is fitted with a controllable pitch 4-bladed propeller of KaMeWa design and a balanced streamlined rudder.

The engine room and accommodation are situated aft. She has three masthouses with three unstayed masts; a lookout position comprising a post with crow's nest is situated on the forecastle deck. She also has a combined radar and signal mast integral with the funnel which is of modern streamlined appearance. The ship's resultant profile presents a clean-cut and pleasing picture.

LIST OF HULL SUB-CONTRACTORS

ITEM	*SUB-CONTRACTORS*
Accommodation Insulation . . .	Fibreglass Ltd.
Accommodation Ladders . . .	Tyne Gangway & Co. Ltd.
Air Compressor	Atlas Copco (Gt. Britain) Ltd.
Air Conditioning and Mechanical Ventilation.	Thermotank Limited
Aluminium Painting Raft . . .	Marine Aluminium Aanensen & Co. Ltd.
Anchors and Cables	W. L. Byers & Co. Ltd.
Awnings.	Modern Structural Plastics (Scotland) Ltd.
Bilge and Ballast Control System .	Dobbie McInnes Ltd.
Blocks	Taylor Pallister Ltd.
Boats and Outfit	Arbuthnott & Son
Boat Davits	Schat Davits Ltd.
Cafeteria.	A/S Edco
Calorifier.	Dugald McCallum Ltd.
Casing Insulation	Reid, Parker & Co. Ltd.
Compasses and Nautical Instruments .	B. Cooke & Sons Ltd. and Henry Browne & Son. Ltd
Cooking Apparatus	Beha Hedo A/S, Didr. Andersen & Son A/S, Hobart Manufacturing Co. Ltd.
Deck Covering	Rowan & Boden
Deck Machinery	The Norwinch Group
Domestic Pressure System . . .	Johan Troye A/S
Domestic Refrigerators. . . .	Turner & Co. (Glasgow) Ltd.
Drinking Water Coolers . . .	Turner & Co. (Glasgow) Ltd.
Electrical Installation	Scotts' Shipbuilding Co. (1969) Ltd.
Emergency Fire Pump	Drysdale & Co. Ltd.
Fire Extinguishing Installation . .	John Kerr & Co. (Manchester) Ltd.
Fire Detection System	Miller Insulation & Engineering Ltd
Hatch Covers.	MacGregor & Co. (Naval Architects) Ltd.
Hospital Berths	Hoskins & Sons Ltd.
Laundry Equipment	A/S Thune Maskiner
Liferafts.	Walter Tangen A/S
Lifesaving Appliances	Seadog Life Saving Appliances Ltd.
Mooring Wires, Hawsers & Warps .	Martin Black & Co. (Wire Ropes) Ltd.
Nameplates	Rennie & Co. Ltd.
Paint Materials	Monopol Maling, W. & J. Leigh Ltd.
Refrigerated Chamber Insulation .	McEwan Insulators Ltd.
Refrigeration Machinery . . .	J. & E. Hall Ltd.
Rigging Shackles and Screws . .	Wood & Clark
Rudder Carrier	John Hastie & Co. Ltd.
Sanitary Fittings	Shanks & Co. Ltd.
Sewage System	Hamworthy Engineering Ltd.
Sheet Iron and Stainless Steel . .	Fawkes & Sorbie Ltd.
Ships Bells	William Hume & Co. Ltd.

ITEM	SUB-CONTRACTORS
Sidelights	Wood & Clark Ltd.
Steel Derricks	Stewarts & Lloyds Ltd.
Steel Castings	Taylor Pallister Ltd. & A/S Moss Vaerft & Dokk
Steering Gear	John Hastie & Co. Ltd.
Sternframe, Rudder and Rudderstock.	A/S Strommens Vaerksted
Tiling	A. De Cecco Ltd.
Upholstery and Furnishings. . .	Rowan & Boden Ltd.
Windows	Wood & Clark Ltd.
Window Wipers	Wynstruments Ltd.
Velle Cranes	Cargospeed Equipment Ltd.

LIST OF MACHINERY SUB-CONTRACTORS

ITEM	SUPPLIER
Main Engines.	Burmeister & Wain
Gearbox and Clutches	Renk
Variable Pitch Propeller . . .	Stone Manganese Marine
Diesel Alternators.	Davey Paxman & Co. and N.E.B.B.
Shaft Driven Alternators . . .	N.E.B.B.
Main Switchboard.	Campbell & Isherwood
Control Console	Contropanels
S.W. Circ. Pump	Drysdale
Bilge Pump	Drysdale
General Service Pump	Drysdale
Ballast Pumps	Drysdale
Oily Water Separator	Alexander Esplen
Oily Water Separator Pump. . .	Drysdale
Fresh Water Generator. . . .	G. & J. Weir
Fresh Water Generator Pump . .	Drysdale
Lub. Oil Pumps	Drysdale
Lub. Oil Suction Filters . . .	J. G. Kincaid & Co.
Lub. Oil Discharge Filters . . .	Scamco
Lub. Oil Byepass Filters . . .	Alexander Leith
Lub. Oil Coolers	Serck Radiators
Turbocharger Lub. Oil Pumps . .	Burmeister & Wain
Turbocharger L.O. Pump Disch. Filter	Burmeister & Wain
Camshaft Lub. Oil Pumps . . .	Drysdale
Camshaft L.O. Pump Discharge Filter	Scamco
Lub. Oil Purifiers	Alfa-Laval
Lub. Oil Purifier Heaters . . .	Heatrae Ltd.
Gearbox Lub. Oil Pumps . . .	Burmeister & Wain
Gearbox Lub. Oil Filter . . .	Burmeister & Wain
Gearbox Lub. Oil Cooler . . .	Burmeister & Wain

ITEM	SUPPLIER
Fuel Oil Surcharge Pumps . . .	Drysdale
Heavy Fuel Oil Transfer Pump . .	Drysdale
Diesel Fuel Purifier	Drysdale
Heavy Fuel Oil Purifiers . . .	Alfa-Laval
Heavy Fuel Purifier Heater . . .	Heatrae Ltd.
Diesel Fuel Purifier	Alfa-Laval
Fuel Valve Coolant Pumps . . .	Drysdale
Fuel Valve Coolers	Serck Radiators Ltd.
Heavy Fuel Oil Return Receiver . .	John G. Kincaid & Co. Ltd.
Sludge Pump	Comet
Heavy Oil Heat Exchangers. . .	Alfa-Laval
Heavy Oil Circ. Pumps. . . .	Drysdale
Heavy Oil Heaters.	Heatrae Ltd.
Water Heated Outflow Heaters . .	J. G. Kincaid & Co.
Hot Water Circ. Pump	Drysdale
Water Heater	Heatrae Ltd.
F.W. Circ. Pumps	Drysdale
F.W. Transfer Pump	Drysdale
F.W. Coolers	Alfa-Laval
Magnetic Water Conditioner . .	Olaf Fjeldsend
Main Air Compressors	Hamworthy
Main Air Reservoirs	J. G. Kincaid & Co.
Emergency Air Compressors . .	Hamworthy
Diesel Alternator Air Receiver . .	Davey Paxman & Co. Ltd.
Whistles	Industrial & Mining Supplies Co. Ltd.
Vent Fans	Wood Fans Ltd.
Purifier Vent Fan	Wood Fans Ltd.
Lathe	Rollo Industrial Co.
Drilling Machine (Elliot-Progress) .	Rollo Industrial Co.
Grinder	Rollo Industrial Co.
Main Eng. Fuel Oil Heaters . . .	Heatrae Ltd.
Main Eng. Silencers	J. G. Kincaid & Co.
Alarm System	Soren T. Lyngso
Tachometer Equipment	
(Main Engines)	Soren T. Lyngso
Exhaust Gas Monitors	
(Main Engines)	Soren T. Lyngso
Shut Down Panels (Main Engines) .	Soren T. Lyngso
Shut Down Panels	
(Diesel Alternators)	Soren T. Lyngso
Pneumatic Control Equipment . .	Westinghouse Hannover
Telegraph	Kwant Bros.
Tachometer Equipment (Shaft) . .	Rheintacho
Temperature Control Equipment	
(S.W. & F.W.)	Ronald Trist Controls Ltd.
Propellor Load Control . . .	Stone Manganese Marine

Appendix 2

Details of ships referred to in text and photographs

Name	Gross Tons /Year built	Owner	Disposal/Year
Achilles	2,362/1866	Alfred Holt & Co.	Scrapped – 1899.
Agamemnon	2,291/1865	Nederland Stomvaarts Maats 'Ocean'	Scrapped – 1899.
Ajax	2,384/1866	Nederland	Scrapped – 1900.
Archibald Russell (Sailing Vessel)	2,385/1905	J. Hardie & Co.	Scrapped – 1949.
Arrow (Sailing Vessel)	3,090/1902	Anglo-American Oil Co. Ltd.	Parma – 12, Reduced to a hulk – 1936.
Ayrshire	9,360/1957	Scottish Shire Line	Total Loss – 1965.
Baknes	13,241/1970	H.C. Clarkson & Co.	Silver Clyde – 1974, Argo Clyde – 1979, Chios Proto – 1980, Topaz – 1981, Lapis – 1982, Industrial Strength – 1984, Fidelity Trust – 1989.
Banbury	11,381/1971	Alexander Shipping	Iron Banbury – 1975, Lady Marina –1982, Ariane S. – 1988.
Ben Ocean Lancer (Drill ship)	10,823/1972	Ben Odeco Ltd., U.K	Lancer – 1991.
Bonaventure	*5,490/1940	H.M. Cruiser	Torpedoed & Sunk – 31/3/41.
British Tweed	15,538/1973	B.P. Tanker Co.,	B.P.Tweed – 1985, Aznar – 1986.
Cachalot	*2,030/1959	H.M. Submarine	Scrapped – 1980.
Caledonia	623/1934	Caledonian Steam Packet Co. Ltd.	Old Caledonia – 1971. Suffered extensive fire damage while floating restaurant and scrapped – 1981.
Challenger (Diving support)	*6,400/1984	Royal Navy	
Chanchow	9,511/1951	China Navigation Co.	Resurgent – 1951, Scrapped – 1981.
Chieftain	223/1930	Steel & Bennie Ltd.	St. Eval – 1968.

Name	Gross Tons /Year built	Owner	Disposal/Year
Chunking	9,301/1950	China Navigation Co.	Retainer – 1952, Scrapped – 1980.
Clan Alpine	8,713/1967	Clan Line Steamers Ltd.	African Diamond – 1981, Pacific Amber – 1983, Scrapped – 1984.
Clan Campbell	7,255/1937	Clan Line Steamers Ltd.	Bombed & Sunk, 23/3/42.
Clan Grant	9,322/1962	Clan Line Steamers Ltd.	Enriquetta – 1980, Scrapped – 1984.
Clan Maciver	7,413/1958	Clan Line Steamers Ltd.	Trinity Pride – 1979, Scrapped – 1980.
Clan Macgillivray	8,811/1962	Clan Line Steamers Ltd.	Clan MacBoyd – 1981, Scrapped – 1984.
Clan Macgowan	9,039/1963	Clan Line Steamers Ltd.	Indian Tribune – 1970, Scrapped – 1985.
Clan Macgregor	9,039/1962	Clan Line Steamers Ltd.	Angelika R – 1981, Scrapped – 1983.
Clan Malcolm	7,554/1957	Clan Line Steamers Ltd.	Trinity Fair – 1979, Scrapped – 1979.
Clan Ramsay	10,542/1965	Clan Line Steamers Ltd.	Winchester Castle – 1977, Winchester Universal – 1980, Lady Madonna – 1981, Scrapped – 1985.
Clan Ranald	10,541/1965	Clan Line Steamers Ltd.	Dover Castle – 1977, Dover Universal – 1979, Golden Sea – 1981, Scrapped – 1985.
Clan Robertson	10,542/1965	Clan Line Steamers Ltd.	Balmoral Castle – 1977, Balmoral Universal – 1979, Psara Refeer – 1982, Scrapped – 1984.

Name	Gross Tons /Year built	Owner	Disposal/Year
Clan Ross	10,541/1966	Clan Line Steamers Ltd.	Kinpurnie Castle – 1977, Kinpurnie Universal – 1979, Syros Reefer – 1982, Scrapped – 1984.
Clarkspey	7,683/1960	H. Clarkson & Co.	Port Campbell – 1961, Kings Reach – 1966, Alderminster – 1970, Jol – 1976, Flora C – 1976, Scrapped – 1982.
Clydesdale	24,024/1967	Hadley Sg. Co.	Clyde Bridge – 1969, Dunster Grange – 1979, Gulf Kehral – 1982, Five Star – 1983, Scrapped – 1986.
Comte de Smet de Naeyer	1,863/1905 (net)	Association Maritime Belge	Total Loss – 1906.
Dawnlight 1	199/165	Ross & Marshall Ltd.	The Marisco – 1987
Devon Coast	972/1937	Coast Lines Ltd.	Windsor Queen – 1963, Elca – 1965, Eleni R – 1967, Scrapped – 1973.
Drakenstein	6,837/1964	South African Marine Corp.	S.A.Drakenstein – 1966, Drakenstein – 1977, Pampero Universal – 1979, Aegean Wave –1980, Scrapped –1984.
Durrington	7,500/1981	Stephenson Clarke Shipping Ltd.	
Falaba	7,703/1962	Elder Dempster Lines Ltd.	Leanor Marie – 1978, Alexander's Trust – 1980, City of Zug –1983, Scrapped –1984.
Fort Austin	*17,000/1979	Royal Fleet Auxiliary	

Name	Gross Tons /Year built	Owner	Disposal/Year
Fort Grange	*17,000/1978	Royal Fleet Auxiliary	
Fourah Bay	7,704/1961	Elder Dempster Lines Ltd.	Magda Josefina – 1978, Alexander's Faith – 1980, Lemina – 1984, Scrapped – 1984.
Geestcape	8,042/1966	Geest Industries Ltd.	Nyombe – 1975, Turtle – 1981, Total Loss – 1983.
Geesthaven	8,042/1966	Geest Industries Ltd.	Doha – 1976, Scrapped – 1986.
Geestland	5,871/1972	Geest Industries Ltd.	Starland – 1986.
Geeststar	5,871/1973	Geest Industries Ltd.	Frio Brazil – 1986.
Glenfinlas	13,298/1966	Glen Line Ltd.	Phemius – 1973, Kweichow – 1979, Saudi Kawther – 1983, Scrapped –1985.
Graigwerrd	18,618/1964	Idwal Williams & Co. Ltd.	Anthony – 1974, Epta Dafnes –1981, Lilian –1983, Scrapped – 1985.
Hyatt	*2,030/1976	Chilean Navy	
Kapetan Georgis	17,059/1963	Virgo S.S. Co. Ltd.	Scrapped – 1986.
Kong Haakon VII	109,423/1969	Hilmar Reksten	Scrapped – 1984.
Letaba	6,661/1963	South African Marine Corp.	S.A. Letaba – 1966, Letaba – 1977, Passat Universal – 1979, Africa Freezer – 1981, Scrapped –1985.
Lord Codrington	9,364/1958	Norships Ocean Carriers Ltd.	Arma – 1968, Agia Varvara – 1976, Felicity – 1984, Scrapped – 1984.
Lord of the Isles	3,504/1989	Caledonian MacBrayne	
Maidstone (Sub. Depot)	*3,600/1912	Royal Navy	Disposed of – 1929.

Name	Gross Tons /Year built	Owner	Disposal/Year
Makrana	8,764/1957	T. & J. Brocklebank Ltd.	*Aegis Glory* – 1971, *Aegis Eternity* – 1971, Scrapped – 1974.
Maron	16,482/1980	Ocean Transport & Trading Ltd.	*Studland Bay* – 1983, *Maron* – 1986, *Baltic Adventurer* – 1986, *Rainbow Avenue* – 1986, *Merchant Patriot* – 1988, *C.M.B. Enterprise* – 1989, *Woermann Triumph* – 1991.
Mentor	16,482/1980	Ocean Transport & Trading Ltd.	*City of London* – 1983, *Mentor* – 1984, *Normannia* – 1985, *Als Reliance* – 1986, *Hoegh Normania* – 1989.
Myrmidon	16,484/1980	Ocean Transport & Trading Ltd.	*Cape Town Carrier* – 1984, *Myrmidon* – 1986, *Bella Folawiyo* – 1986, *C.M.B. Exporter* – 1989.
Norfolk	* 3,500/1990	Royal Navy	
Opportune	* 2,030/1964	Royal Navy	
Otama	* 2,030/1978	Australian Navy	
Otter	* 2,030/1962	Royal Navy	Paid off – 1990.
Otus	* 2,030/1963	Royal Navy	
Otway	* 2,030/1968	Australian Royal Navy	
Oxley	* 2,030/1967	Australian Royal Navy	
Parma	5,590/1967	F. Laeisz	*Parma 11* – 1973, *F. Freiligrath* – 1975, *Apple Blossom* – 1990.
Prome	7,043/1937	British & Burmese Steam Nav. Co.	Scrapped – 1962.

Name	Gross Tons /Year built	Owner	Disposal/Year
Queen Elizabeth 2	65,863/1968	Cunard Steamship Co., Ltd.	
Queen Mary	81,237/1936	Cunard Steamship Co., Ltd.	Sold to city of Long Beach, California – 1967.
Raylight	177/1963	Ross & Marshall Ltd.	Total Loss – 1975.
Resource	*22,890/1966	Royal Fleet Auxiliary	
Rotherwick Castle	9,650/1959	Union Castle Mail S.S. Co.	Sea Fortune – 1976, Silver Rays – 1980, Scrapped – 1982.
Rothesay Castle	9,650/1960	Union Castle Mail S.S. Co.	Laura – 1976, Scrapped – 1980.
S1 (Submarine)	*255/1914	Royal Navy	Sold – 1915, to Italian Navy.
San Vicente	4,928/1975	San Vicente Partners Ltd.	Oscar C – 1989.
Simandou	10,764/1963	Enterprise De Transport Nationale Routier	Athina – 1980, Scrapped – 1984.
Sugar Carrier	17,775/1974	Sugar Line Ltd.	Patricia – 1981, Continental Charterer – 1986, Teapotzlan – 1990, Glastnos – 1990.
Swan River	9,367/1959	Houlder Bros. & Co. Ltd.	Premier Atlantic – 1972, Confidence Express – 1974, Bachlong – 1979, Eastern Concord – 1980, Scrapped – 1983.
Torch	329/1924	Clyde Navigation Trust	Scrapped – 1978.
Tzaneen	6,837/1964	South African Marine Corp.	S.A. Tzaneen – 1966, Tzaneen – 1977, Papagayo Universal – 1979, Scrapped – 1985.
Walrus	* 2,030/1961	Royal Navy	Paid Off – 1987.
Waverley	693/1947	Waverley Steam Navigation Co. Ltd.	
World President	12,341/1969	World Wide Shipping Co. Ltd.	Erisort – 1972, Prabhu Satram – 1977.

Name	Gross Tons /Year built	Owner	Disposal/Year
World Hong Kong	12,341/1969	Marine Navigation Co. Ltd. (World Wide Shipping)	*Eriboll* – 1973, *Anadria* – 1979, *Red Deer* – 1989, Scrapped – 1991.
Wrestler	192/1915	Steel & Bennie Ltd.	*Irene Lamey* – 1954, Scrapped 1964.
Wrestler	248/1957	Hall & Barrie Ltd.	Creta Salvor – 1979.

* = Displacement tons

Index

127